The ARRL Guide to
Antenna Tuners

A Radio Amateur's Guide to Antenna Matching

Joel R. Hallas, W1ZR

On the Cover

The group of special purpose antenna tuners made by the late George Badger, W6TC, is shown beneath his rotary antenna system. The inset shows a general purpose L-network antenna tuner built by Barry Shackleford, W6YE, who took both photos. Both are discussed in Chapter 15.

Production
Michelle Bloom, WB1ENT
Jodi Morin, KA1JPA
David Pingree, N1NAS

Cover
Sue Fagan, KB1OKW

Foreword

Antenna Tuners are mystical devices that are sometimes needed between antenna systems and transmission lines or radios to make everything play the way it's supposed to. They are the subject of considerable confusion and misunderstanding by many Amateur Radio operators.

This book is intended to assist readers who have a basic knowledge of antennas, such as conveyed by *Basic Antennas — Understanding Practical Antennas and Designs*, in gaining an understanding of whether or not they need an antenna tuner in their station.[1] If it turns out one is needed, this book will help the reader decide the type of tuner needed and where in the system it should be applied. Also provided are descriptions of appropriate applications of such devices and antennas that are well suited for such use. An additional chapter provides data collected from ARRL Laboratory product reviews of representative antenna tuners to assist in tuner selection. Design methodology and specific design details are also provided for those who wish to build their own tuners.

As with all ARRL books, be sure to check to see if there are any last minute changes that didn't get into the book before it went to the printer. Updates and errata, if any, can be found at **www.arrl. org/product-notes/**.

David Sumner, K1ZZ
Executive Vice President
Newington, Connecticut
October 2010

[1]J. Hallas, W1ZR, *Basic Antennas — Understanding Practical Antennas and Designs,* Available from your ARRL dealer or the ARRL Bookstore, ARRL order no. 9994. Telephone 860-594-0355, or toll-free in the US 888-277-5289; **www.arrl.org/arrl.store/**; **pubsales@arrl.org**.

Acknowledgements

I would like to offer my special thanks to the ARRL production and editorial staff who made this book come together smoothly. In addition, thanks go to my long-suffering wife Nancy, W1NCY, who put up with the countless hours of my writing to make this happen.

I especially appreciated the tireless efforts of ARRL Technical Advisor Barry Shackleford, W6YE, who carefully examined every page of the manuscript in an effort to make sure there were neither technical nor grammatical errors and that all points were made clearly.

About the ARRL

The national association for Amateur Radio

The seed for Amateur Radio was planted in the 1890s, when Guglielmo Marconi began his experiments in wireless telegraphy. Soon he was joined by dozens, then hundreds, of others who were enthusiastic about sending and receiving messages through the air—some with a commercial interest, but others solely out of a love for this new communications medium. The United States government began licensing Amateur Radio operators in 1912.

By 1914, there were thousands of Amateur Radio operators—hams—in the United States. Hiram Percy Maxim, a leading Hartford, Connecticut inventor and industrialist, saw the need for an organization to band together this fledgling group of radio experimenters. In May 1914 he founded the American Radio Relay League (ARRL) to meet that need.

Today ARRL, with approximately 150,000 members, is the largest organization of radio amateurs in the United States. The ARRL is a not-for-profit organization that:
- promotes interest in Amateur Radio communications and experimentation
- represents US radio amateurs in legislative matters, and
- maintains fraternalism and a high standard of conduct among Amateur Radio operators.

At ARRL headquarters in the Hartford suburb of Newington, the staff helps serve the needs of members. ARRL is also International Secretariat for the International Amateur Radio Union, which is made up of similar societies in 150 countries around the world.

ARRL publishes the monthly journal *QST*, as well as newsletters and many publications covering all aspects of Amateur Radio. Its headquarters station, W1AW, transmits bulletins of interest to radio amateurs and Morse code practice sessions. The ARRL also coordinates an extensive field organization, which includes volunteers who provide technical information and other support services for radio amateurs as well as communications for public-service activities. In addition, ARRL represents US amateurs with the Federal Communications Commission and other government agencies in the US and abroad.

Membership in ARRL means much more than receiving *QST* each month. In addition to the services already described, ARRL offers membership services on a personal level, such as the ARRL Volunteer Examiner Coordinator Program and a QSL bureau.

Full ARRL membership (available only to licensed radio amateurs) gives you a voice in how the affairs of the organization are governed. ARRL policy is set by a Board of Directors (one from each of 15 Divisions) elected by the membership. The day-to-day operation of ARRL HQ is managed by a Chief Executive Officer.

No matter what aspect of Amateur Radio attracts you, ARRL membership is relevant and important. There would be no Amateur Radio as we know it today were it not for the ARRL. We would be happy to welcome you as a member! (An Amateur Radio license is not required for Associate Membership.) For more information about ARRL and answers to any questions you may have about Amateur Radio, write or call:

ARRL—The national association for Amateur Radio
225 Main Street
Newington CT 06111-1494
Voice: 860-594-0200
Fax: 860-594-0259
E-mail: **hq@arrl.org**
Internet: **www.arrl.org/**

Prospective new amateurs call (toll-free):
800-32-NEW HAM (800-326-3942)
You can also contact us via e-mail at **newham@arrl.org**
or check out *ARRLWeb* at **http://www.arrl.org/**

Table of Contents

Chapter 1

Why I Might Need an Antenna Tuner

Amateur Radio station W1ZR, home station of the author. The unit on the far left is an early Ten-Tec 238 manual antenna tuner.

Contents

To transmit radio signals, you need a transmitter, often the transmitter side of a *transceiver* — a combined transmitter and receiver — and an antenna. Of course you will need a few other things such as legal authority to transmit, from the FCC in the US, a power source and an information source, such as a telegraph key, microphone or PC. In this book we will focus on the interconnection between the transmitter and the antenna, leaving the other topics to other books.

You might notice that, in spite of the book's title, we didn't mention antenna tuners — a device that goes between the transmitter and antenna. This is because, strictly speaking, an antenna tuner isn't necessary, at least not in all cases. The antenna tuner is only required if the transmitter can't put its output power into the antenna because of an incompatibility between them.

Radio Incompatibility?

A radio transmitter comes with a set of specifications. For proper operation, the owner is responsible to ensure that the requirements listed in the specifications are met. Some are straightforward, such as "power required: 13.8 V dc at 20 A max." If we plugged such a radio into a 120 V ac outlet, we wouldn't have a right to expect it to operate properly — in fact we might expect to see smoke and flames. We would need an intermediate device, called a power supply, to transform the 120 V ac in our outlet to the 13.8 V dc our radio wants.

The compatibility issue we will be considering here is one relating to the ANTENNA IMPEDANCE specification. While not all transmitter specifications include an explicit antenna specification, most will say something like ANTENNA IMPEDANCE, 50 Ω (Unbalanced) or possibly ANTENNA IMPEDANCE, 50 Ω (Unbalanced) with SWR of 2:1 or less. These specifications indicate the load that the antenna system must present to the radio for proper operation. We will discuss the different parts of this specification and what they mean as we go forward. As with the power supply, if the antenna doesn't meet the specification's requirements, we might need an intermediate device — possibly an antenna tuner.

Does My Antenna Have to be a Resistor?

The indication "50 Ω" does sound a lot like a resistor. The radio will be very happy to put its power into an actual 50 Ω resistor, in fact that's how we often test a radio when we don't want the radio signal to go out over the air. Unfortunately, a resistor absorbs the transmitter power and turns it into heat — it does not make a good antenna.

In a properly designed antenna, it is often the case that the antenna's radiating properties will be converted into a load that acts like a 50 Ω resistor to the radio, but actually radiates the power as radio waves.

So What's the Problem?

It would seem that we can solve our incompatibility problem by just buying (or building) an antenna that has a compatible specification of a 50 Ω resistive impedance and connecting it to our radio. This is quite true, and can be very successful — within certain constraints (see **Figure 1-1** for the ideal case). This compatible case is referred to as a *matched* system. Unfortunately, the real world rears its ugly head in a few ways:

• The biggest issue is that any antenna will have its particular design impedance on a single frequency. This is not an issue with many radio services — broadcast stations, for example — that operate on a single assigned frequency. Some services, such as the Amateur Radio service, operate within assigned bands. Shifting frequency from one end of the band to the other can result in a significant

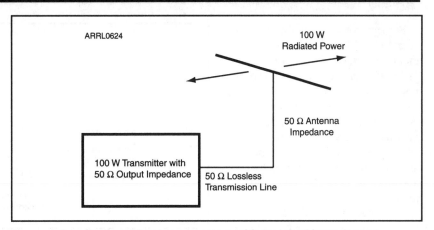

Figure 1-1 — Radio and antenna system with matched impedances.

change in antenna impedance.

• A real antenna is always installed at some height above the local terrain. The electrical properties of the soil and the height above ground will have a significant impact on antenna

impedance. For example, perhaps the simplest antenna, a half wave horizontal dipole has an impedance that varies from around 40 to 100 Ω as it moves from 0.1 to 0.35 λ (wavelengths) above ground.

What Happens if the Radio and Antenna Aren't Matched?

Most radios can tolerate a certain amount of mismatch from an antenna system without any problems. This is often specified in terms of standing wave ratio (SWR), a measure of mismatch. Often the allowed value is 2:1; which, for a 50 Ω system, would represent resistive values of 25 or 100 Ω (50/2, or 50 × 2).[1] Note that while the radio will operate without

damage at this level of mismatch, it may not operate quite as well as if it were matched.

A mismatched load impedance in early solid state transmitters could result in damage to components in the power amplifier stages due to higher voltages or currents than it was designed to handle. Modern transceivers have *fold-back* circuitry

that senses the mismatch and reduces transmitter power to avoid damage. Note that while the transmitter will not be damaged, and still can be used, it will put out less power, sometimes beginning to fold back at an SWR as low as 1.5:1. This is perhaps the most common reason that we might notice our 100 W transmitter actually putting out 25 W.

[1]In addition to these two resistive values, there is a whole set of combinations of resistive and reactive impedance components that will also result in an SWR of 2:1.

So What Can We Do?

Perhaps not surprisingly, one solution to this issue is something that is generally called an *antenna tuner*. The antenna tuner is a variable impedance transforming device that can transform the impedance of an antenna system so that it appears to the transmitter as a 50 Ω load, while causing almost all of the transmitter power to be radiated from the antenna, just as if everything were matched.

As shown in **Figure 1-2**, the antenna tuner can be placed directly at the transmitter and connect directly to an antenna. In many cases, a *transmission line* is used between the transmitter and the antenna. We will discuss transmission lines in more detail later, but for now be aware that a transmission line is frequently used if the transmitter and antenna are not in the same place. As shown in **Figures 1-3** and **1-4**, the antenna tuner can be placed at either the antenna end or the radio end of a transmission line interconnecting the radio and antenna. It could even be put at an intermediate point.

Much of this book will discuss the details of the different configurations and requirements of antenna tuners and where they are located, so you can make the most informed decision on what type of tuner to buy or build and where to install it.

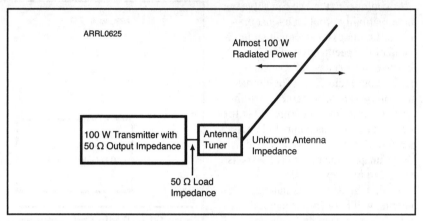

Figure 1-2 — Antenna tuner collocated with the radio and the antenna. All the transmitter power reaches the antenna except for any loss in the tuner, generally less than 5%.

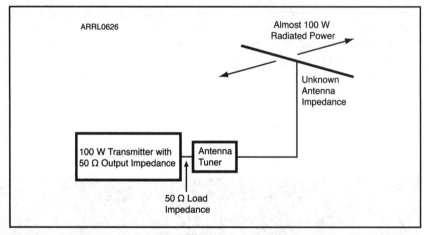

Figure 1-3 — Radio and antenna system with tuner located at the radio end of the transmission line.

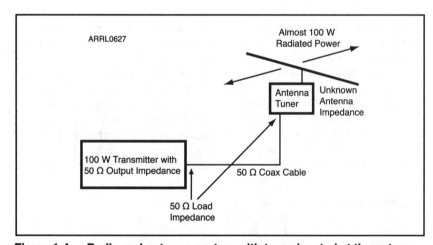

Figure 1-4 — Radio and antenna system with tuner located at the antenna end of the transmission line.

What's in a Name?

Over the years there has been some discussion of what to call this device I call an *antenna tuner*. There are those who would say that *antenna tuner* is a misnomer because it doesn't actually tune the antenna, but really tunes the transmission line in most applications.

Over the years many other terms have been used to describe this device. You will see references to an *antenna coupler*, *antenna tuning unit* (ATU) and a *transmatch* — all within various ARRL magazines and books. They all mean the same thing and refer to the same type of device.

The best name I've heard for this function is *antenna system matching device*. Since that doesn't resolve itself to an easy to pronounce acronym, throughout this book I will use the most common term *antenna tuner* with neither apology nor regret.

Review Questions

1-1 Under what conditions is there no requirement for an antenna tuner in a transmitting system?

1-2 How can you tell if an antenna tuner is needed?

1-3 What are the likely consequences of not having an antenna tuner, or having a misadjusted antenna tuner?

1-4 If an antenna tuner is properly adjusted on one frequency, what must be done if the operating frequency is changed?

Chapter 2

A Look at Typical Configurations

The classic half-wave dipole — an antenna mainstay at many amateur stations.

Contents

A very popular antenna for a new radio amateur is called a *half-wave dipole*. This antenna is easy to construct from two pieces of wire with a total length of about 468/f, where f is the frequency in MHz and the result is in feet. The antenna is often fed with 50 Ω coaxial cable as shown in **Figure 2-1**. Generally, the antenna length is trimmed equally on each side of center until the closest match to 50 Ω is found. While it will function as shown, more predictable performance is often obtained by inserting a device between the inherent-ly balanced antenna and unbalanced (with respect to ground) coaxial cable to provide an appropriate transition between them. This device is gener-ally called a balun — for balanced to unbalanced transition. We will discuss this in detail later in the book.

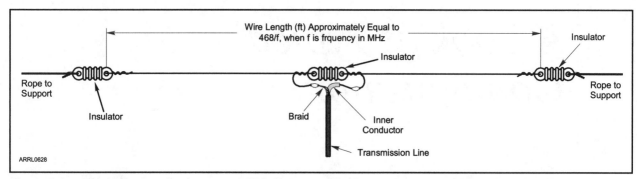

Figure 2-1 — The half wave dipole antenna. This is a very effective antenna, considering its ease of construction and low cost.

A Transmission Line — The Piece in the Middle

In most cases the antenna and radio are located in separate areas. Most often, the optimum location for the radio is somewhere that a person can comfortably operate a radio. For many types of radio systems, this means indoors. The antenna, on the other hand, is typically located outside so it can radiate with minimal obstructions and with at optimum height above the terrain.

It is possible to meet both require-ments if an antenna is connected to the radio system through a *transmission line*. An ideal transmission line conveys energy from one end to the other in a totally transparent manner. A real transmission line, on the other hand does so with some limitations:

• Each type of transmission line has a characteristic impedance, Z_0. If the transmission line is terminated with an impedance equal to the Z_0, the same impedance will be seen at any length of line. Fortunately, there are many types of line that have a Z_0 of 50 Ω, so such a line connected to an antenna with a 50 Ω impedance will present a 50 Ω load to the radio no matter the length of the line. It is worth mentioning briefly at this point that if the line is terminated in an impedance other than its Z_0, the im-pedance at the far end in general will be neither the terminating impedance nor the Z_0 of the line.

These topics will be covered in much more detail later, but it's good to have an idea as we go through the basics.

• Real transmission lines have some associated losses. Thus not all the power put into the bottom by the transmitter comes out at the antenna. The attenuation is higher with increasing frequency, for a given type of line. The attenuation is also directly proportional to line length. In addition, the attenuation increases with standing wave ratio (SWR, a measure of mismatch) — another reason to have a matched system, if possible. We will discuss this phe-nomenon later.

• SWR is generally determined by measuring the ratio of reflected power to forward power. An SWR of 1:1 re-sults in no reflected power. If the line has significant attenuation, both the power getting to the antenna, and any reflected power will be attenuated. Thus a measurement of SWR at the radio end will appear to be lower than the real SWR at the antenna end.

Dipole for the 40 Meter Amateur Band

If we were to make a dipole of the form of Figure 2-1 for the center of the US 40 meter band, we would use the formula 468/f, with the f equal to 7.15 MHz to result in a starting length of 65.45 feet, or 65 feet, 5.4 inches. As noted previously, this will vary with height, but let's say we get it all correct and have a height that provides close to a 50 Ω load at that frequency. If we then measure the

standing wave ratio (SWR) across the band, 7.0 – 7.3 MHz, we would observe a set of SWR data very much like that plotted in **Figure 2-2**.[1,2]

Note that, as desired, we observe an almost perfectly matched condition (SWR of 1:1) at our design frequency of 7.15 MHz. Note also that as we change frequency across the

[1]Notes appear on page 6.

band, our SWR rises to 2:1 at each band edge. Thus, even though our antenna is only closely matched at the band center, if the transmitter can operate at full power with a 2:1 SWR, this antenna will be usable across the band, if trimmed very carefully.

What About Height?

We have previously mentioned that changing height will also change the

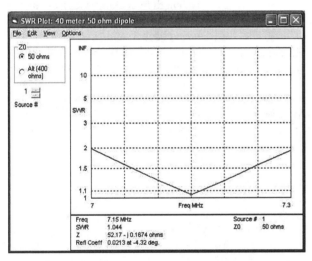

Figure 2-2 — Plot of SWR of a 40 meter dipole with height and length adjusted for 50 Ω at 7.15 MHz.

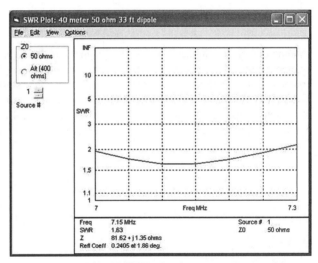

Figure 2-3 — Plot of SWR of a 40 meter dipole with height set to λ/4, about 33 feet.

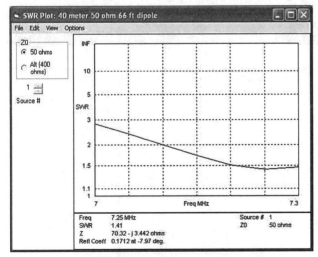

Figure 2-4 — Plot of SWR of 40 meter dipole of Figure 2-3 raised to a height of λ/2, about 66 feet. Note the change in frequency of minimum SWR. It could be tuned back to mid-band by lengthening.

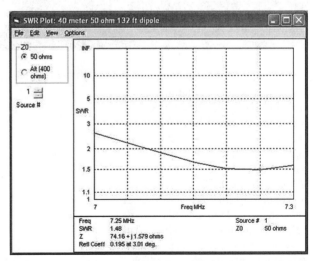

Figure 2-5 — Plot of same antenna raised to 1 λ, about 132 feet.

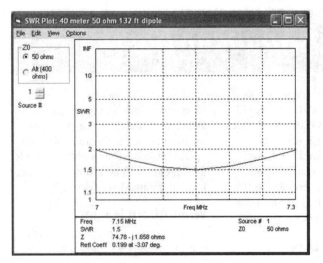

angle radiation to support communication over longer distances.

Impedance and Resonant Frequency at Greater Height

Figs 2-3 through **2-5** are a series of SWR plots of the same antenna as it is raised, first to 33 feet (λ/4), then 66 feet (λ/2) and finally 132 feet (1 λ). Observe the two phenomena happening as the antenna is raised — first, the impedance is changing and second the resonant frequency (frequency at which the impedance is resistive) is changing. Note that the impedance shown is that close to the resonant frequency.

To improve the SWR, we can adjust the length by making it long enough so that the resonant frequency is moved back to mid band. The result is shown in **Figure 2-6**. Note that the antenna now has an SWR range across the band of 2:1 or less so it might still work well across the band without a tuner. Note that to achieve this result, it must be very carefully trimmed.

antenna impedance. In fact it will also change the resonant frequency of the antenna. To obtain the plot in Figure 2-2, we lowered the antenna to a height of 12 feet. While such an antenna will operate, the combination of its direct signal and the signal reflected from the ground will result in most of the radiation going skyward. This makes it suitable for short and medium range communication. In many cases antennas are raised higher to increase low

A Dipole for the 80 Meter Amateur Band

A dipole for 80 meters (don't worry, this is the last example) has a very different result. The US 80 meter (sometimes called 75 and 80 meters) band is wider than 40 meters, covering 3.5 to 4 MHz. The result, again with the height lowered and length adjusted to match 50 Ω at mid band is shown in **Figure 2-7**. This is a very different result from our 40 meter dipole's impedance over the band. The SWR at the band edges is now above 7:1, and the bandwidth over which the SWR is 2:1 or less, the SWR bandwidth, is about 150 kHz — about half what it was on 40 meters.

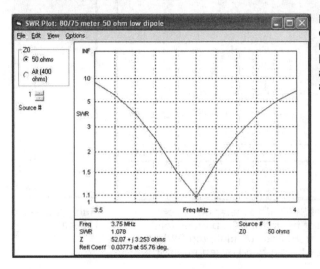

Figure 2-7 — Plot of SWR of a 80/75 meter dipole with height and length adjusted for 50 Ω at 3.75 MHz.

Fractional Bandwidth

The reduced bandwidth on 80 meters illustrates a few interesting principles. First, for a band this wide at this frequency, it would take at least three dipoles with slightly different lengths to cover the whole band if we didn't have a device to transform the impedance to a value we wanted — an *antenna tuner*. Second, we note that the key factor is not the bandwidth itself, but rather the fraction (or percentage) of the center frequency that we wish to be able to cover.

In the case of 40 meters, we were able to cover a bandwidth (7300 – 7000) of 300 kHz with an SWR of 2:1. This is the fraction 300/7150 = 0.042, or 4.2%. Note that on 80 meters we had about 150/3750 = 4%. We can use this as a predictor of whether a single thin dipole can cover each amateur band with the results shown in Table 2-1.

Clearly, the problem is most pronounced on 80 meters, perhaps why we chose that example. In addition, 160, 10 and 6 meters are wider than our threshold, as is the 70 cm band. Fortunately, the higher three of these bands have operations divided by mode, so that it is not unreasonable to have, for example, a horizontal 6 meter antenna centered at the low end for CW and SSB operation and a separate vertical antenna for FM designed for the high end. Many operators, however, like to work all portions of 160 and 80 meters, so that can be an issue.

Table 2-1

Percentage Bandwidth of Each HF and VHF US Amateur Band.

Band (Meters)	Upper Frequency (kHz)	Lower Frequency (kHz)	Bandwidth (kHz)	Bandwidth (%)
160	2000	1800	200	10.5
80	4000	3500	500	13.3
60	5407	5330	77	1.4
40	7300	7000	300	4.2
30	10,100	10,150	50	0.5
20	14,000	14,350	350	2.5
17	18,068	18,168	100	0.6
15	21,000	21,450	450	2.1
12	24,890	24,990	100	0.4
10	28,000	29,700	1700	5.9
6	50,000	54,000	4000	7.7
2	144,000	148,000	4000	2.7
1.25	222,000	225,000	3000	1.3
70 cm	420,000	450,000	30,000	6.9

Notes

[1]This plot was obtained using an antenna modeling program named *EZNEC*. We will call upon this program repeatedly throughout the book. Several versions of *EZNEC* antenna modeling software, including a free trial version, are available from developer Roy Lewallen, W7EL, at **www.eznec.com**.

[2]For an introduction to *EZNEC* modeling, see Appendix A of J. Hallas, W1ZR, *Basic Antennas — Understanding Practical Antennas and Design*. Available from your ARRL dealer or the ARRL Bookstore, ARRL order no. 9994. Telephone 860-594-0355, or toll-free in the US 888-277-5289; **www.arrl.org/arrl-store; pubsales@ arrl.org**. See chapters 2-6.

Review Questions

2-1 Under what conditions might a ½ wave dipole not be compatible with a radio system?

2-2 Why can a transmission line tend to mask a high SWR?

2-3 If a dipole should be able to cover a complete amateur band, but doesn't because the minimum SWR is higher than the middle of the band, what can you do to improve the situation?

2-4 If you have no antenna tuner, how many separate dipoles would be required to cover the entire 10 meter amateur band with an SWR of less than 2:1?

Chapter 3

So Just What Is an Antenna Tuner?

On the left, inside view of a manually tuned 1500 W L-network HF tuner (Ten-Tec 238); on the right, a computer controlled 100 W automatic tuner (Elecraft KAT3) designed to fit inside the compact Elecraft K-3 HF and 6 meter transceiver.

Contents

As noted in Chapter 1, *the antenna tuner is a variable impedance transforming device that can transform the impedance of an antenna system to appear to the transmitter as a 50 Ω load, while causing almost all of the transmitter power to be radiated from* the antenna, *just as if everything were matched.* This sounds like just what we need to solve the problem of using an antenna system that has an SWR that the transmitter doesn't like to deal with.

While an antenna tuner may well be just what we need — they come in many flavors, shapes and sizes — not to mention specification ratings. Much of this book will deal with how to choose the best type of antenna tuner, as well as to determine the best place in the system to locate it.

What's In an Antenna Tuner?

In order to perform its transformation function, an antenna tuner must deal with any load that is within its specified limits (everything has its limits — no antenna tuner can match absolutely everything!). As noted in the sidebar, an SWR greater than 1:1 happens if the load of the antenna system is different from the specified output load impedance of the transmitter, 50 Ω for most current designs. Table B in the sidebar shows some representative values of resistance and capacitive or inductive series reactance that result in various values of SWR.

Note that we could categorize the load impedance into four general categories that could all have different solutions:

1. The load is a resistive impedance of 50 Ω. In this case the SWR is 1:1 and we don't need an antenna tuner at all. We could bundle with this all loads that work well with the transmitter without change — perhaps those with an SWR of less than 2:1. There may be a bit of extra loss here or there, but generally everything will work well.

2. The load is a resistive impedance other than 50 Ω , and not close enough to allow proper operation. This could be loads with a 2:1 SWR such as 25 Ω or 100 Ω, a 3:1 SWR such as 16.7 Ω or 150 Ω, or a 10:1 SWR such as 5 Ω or 500 Ω. All of these loads share the fact that they could be matched through the use of an ideal transformer, just as you would match an 8 Ω speaker to a 600 Ω audio line with an audio transformer.

For use in radio rather than audio frequencies, such transformers must be constructed differently to avoid also introducing reactive components, but the approach is feasible and sometimes encountered. One classic example is the matching arrangement employed in a wideband antenna often used at HF called a rhombic. It of-fers an almost resistive load of around 600 Ω over a 4:1 frequency range and is often fed through a wideband 12:1 impedance ratio transformer by a 50 Ω system. **Figure 3-1** shows the idea. While most folks would call it a transformer rather than an antenna tuner, there's no question that it is performing one possible class of the function we're talking about.

3. The load is composed of a combination of a 50 Ω resistive component and a series reactance. A load with a parallel reactance can be transformed into one with a series reactance, but we'll focus on the series version since it may be easier to visualize.

This makes for an easy to imagine antenna tuner. If the series reactance of the load is inductive ($+X_L$), all the antenna tuner need contain is a component with a capacitive reactance of the same magnitude, ($-X_C$). The series combination of the two is just 0 Ω reactive, so the resultant is the

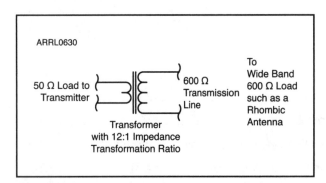

Figure 3-1 — A wide-band impedance transformer can serve the function of an antenna tuner for a resistive load.

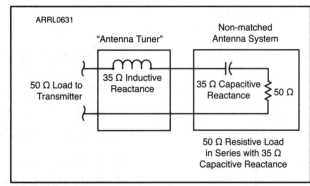

Figure 3-2 — Antenna tuner for special case of reactance in series with resistive part equal to Z_0.

resistive component —50 Ω as shown in **Figure 3-2**.

Note that, unlike the wideband transformer, this will likely work only on a single frequency. If the antenna has an inductive reactance, it will tend to increase with frequency ($X_L = 2 \times \pi \times f \times L$), at least over a limited frequency range. In order to keep the total impedance resistive, we will need a variable capacitor, so we can adjust the capacitive reactance to match the changing inductive reactance of the load. Note that our "antenna tuner" now has a knob on the front, and is starting to look more like an antenna tuner.

4. The load is a combination of resistive and reactive components that have an SWR greater than we can deal with and that falls in none of the other three categories. This is the general case — the one all general purpose antenna tuners must deal with, at least over some range of SWR.

There are a number of circuit configurations that can be employed that will do a combination of cancelling the reactance and transforming the resistive impedance. We have cataloged

ARRL0632

(A) Unbalanced Tuned Variable Transformer

(B) L-network for Z < Z₀

(C) L-network for Z > Z₀

(D) π-network

(E) T-network (High-pass)

(F) T-network (Low-pass)

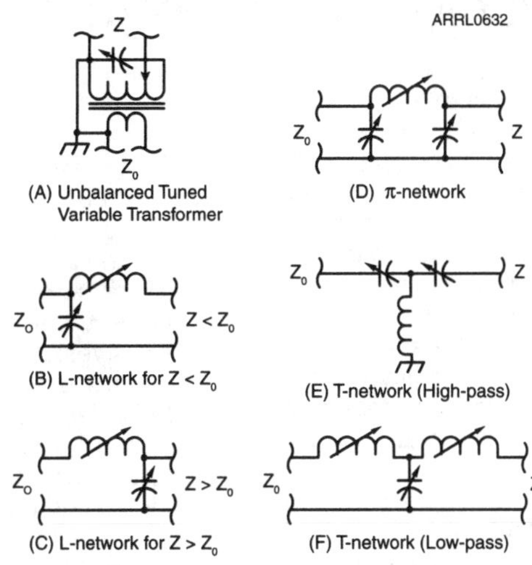

Figure 3-3 — Antenna tuner configurations that can be used to match the more general mismatched load.

them in **Figure 3-3** so you will recognize the configurations as we discuss them. In many cases, if constructed of the same quality components, they will provide equivalent performance. As with all general purpose devices, there are certain advantages and disadvantages of each, and some may be more appropriate for some applications than for others.

Another categorization that can be made is whether the tuner is designed to feed an unbalanced load, typically fed with coaxial cable or a single wire against ground, or is intended to feed a balanced load such as a dipole fed with balanced open wire transmission line. Each of these configurations can be adapted to either task, however, we will defer that discussion until later.

Antenna Tuner Controls

Not surprisingly, many of the different manual antenna tuner configurations have different control arrangements.

L-Network Tuner Controls

The L-network has two primary adjustments, an inductor and a capacitor. In the Ten-Tec 238 tuner shown in **Figure 3-4**, and in most L-network tuners, each control is adjustable throughout its entire range on any band, providing maximum flexibility. In addition, there is a switch to move

Figure 3-4 — Front panel view of an L-network tuner, an early version of the Ten-Tec 238.

A Quick Discussion of Standing Wave Ratio

We discussed standing wave ratio in Chapter 2 and noted that a matched antenna system has a standing wave ratio (SWR) of 1:1. That is the case in which there are no standing waves and all energy from the transmitter is delivered to the load with no reflections on the transmission line. This is a very straightforward situation that is easy to understand. Getting into the details of this topic can get lengthy and there are entire books devoted to the topic.[A] Fortunately, we won't need to get that deeply involved to understand antenna tuners and their applications. Still, we need to have some idea about SWR, what it means and what its consequences are to understand, when and if it is a problem and how to solve it.

The Matched Transmission Line

If we were to connect a battery to a long real transmission line with no load and monitor the current that would flow with a high speed oscilloscope we would notice an interesting effect. The combination of the line series inductance and shunt capacitance, and to a lesser effect the wire resistance, would result in an initial current that would flow, even though there is an open circuit at the far end.

The current will continue to flow until the signal propagates to the end of the line and returns. When it reaches the end of the line (traveling somewhat slower than the speed of light) a *reflected* wave of the opposite polarity will propagate back because there can be no current flow at the open circuit. When the reflected wave returns to the source end of the line the combination of the forward and reflected wave will result in zero current — just what we would expect for an open transmission line.

The ratio of the applied voltage to initial current is an impedance and we call this the characteristic impedance or Z_0 of the transmission line. This is the current that would flow into an infinite length of line no matter what is at the far end. Note that we didn't say anything about signal frequency here, this is strictly a matter of the way the line is constructed, especially the capacitance and inductance that is distributed along its length. For the usual low loss line, ignoring resistance, we can determine Z_0 as follows:

$$Z_0 = \sqrt{L/C}$$

where L and C are the inductance and capacitance per unit length,

typically per foot or per meter. These values can often be found in many manufacturers' specification sheets.

The Matched Transmission Line

If, instead of having an infinite line, we put a resistor with a resistance equal to the line Z_0 on the far end of the line it will absorb the power as it arrives and there will be no reflection. The voltage and current relationship at the signal end of the line will appear as if it were the same resistor, just located at the source.

This is exactly what we wanted! If the source is a radio designed to drive a 50 Ω load, Z_0 is 50 Ω and our load is an antenna with an impedance of 50 Ω, we get just what we want — to our transmitter it appears as if the antenna is connected directly to the antenna. There is no reflected power, the SWR is 1:1 and all is well with the world.

The Mismatched Transmission Line

There are an infinite number of cases in which a transmission line is terminated, not with its Z_0, nor with an open or short, but with some other impedance. This results in a reflection of a signal that is smaller than the signal that was sent down the line. It is important to note that this signal does not represent lost power, because it is re-reflected from the transmitter back up to the line. It is true that the power delivered to the antenna will equal the forward power less the reflected power, however, because the power is re-reflected at the transmitter so the numbers go up together. This is illustrated in **Table A** for the case of perfect (lossless) transmission line, assuming the transmitter can put power into the SWR shown.

So What's the Big Deal

The key is the two reasonable assumptions noted above. Let's discuss each:

■Transmission lines are not lossless, and their losses increase with increasing SWR as we will discuss. Whether or not that's a problem depends on the line

---

Table A

Example of Net Transmitted Power with 100 W Transmitter versus SWR with Lossless Transmission Line

SWR	Reflection %	Forward Power	Reflected Power	Antenna Power
1:1	0	100	0	100
2:1	10	111	11	100
3:1	25	133	33	100

---

the variable capacitor between the two ends of the inductor to allow tuning of both high and low impedance loads.

This particular tuner uses a rotary inductor (see **Figure 3-5**) for adjustment of inductance. The coil turns with rotation of the shaft on the left end. As it turns, its point of connec-

tion to the small wheel on the top in the picture is moved up and down the coil. It requires about 30 turns of the knob to adjust from the minimum to the maximum amount of inductance. Some tuners use a switched inductance instead. The switch allows a quicker change of settings, but does

not provide for values of inductance between the switched taps. This is not generally a problem, although there are some loads that can't be tuned to a 1:1 SWR at some frequencies — still close enough works. Note that there is no bandswitch, on this model, since any available adjustment

type, frequency and SWR as we will discuss later.

■ Often a more serious problem is that somewhere in the range of SWR in Table A, typically by an SWR of 2:1, transmitters will reduce power to avoid damage due to the higher current or voltage that results from the higher than specified SWR.

Note that the second problem is not a fundamental issue of SWR itself, but rather a design choice made by transmitter designers. Still, for transmitters that we may choose to use, it is a real problem that we have to deal with.

What Kind of Load Results in High SWR

Any load that is different from Z_0 of the transmission line will result in a SWR greater than 1:1. For the case of the frequently encountered 50 Ω coaxial cable, that means any load that is not 50 Ω resistive. This can mean a load that is resistive with a value of other than 50 Ω or a load that is resistive, but also has capacitive (–X) or inductive (+X) reactance, or any of an infinite number of combinations of the two. Some examples of loads with different SWRs are shown in **Table B**.

Note that it is very easy to determine the SWR for the resistive case — it's just Z_0/R or R/Z_0 depending on whether the load is greater or less than the Z_0.

Thus it is important to know not just the resistive part, but also the equivalent series inductive or capacitive reactance to determine the SWR.

Determining SWR from Impedance Data

While the case for resistive loads is simple, the case for loads with reactance or complex loads is well — more complex. Still, there are at least three ways that I know of to determine the SWR of a complex load, not counting measuring with an SWR meter, as follows:

■ Use the software TLW (Transmission Line for Windows) that comes packaged with recent editions of The ARRL Antenna Book.[B] If you plug in the R and X values and the appropriate transmission line Z_0, it provides the SWR at each end of the line. You can select which end of the line has the measured Z (input or load). This is very handy since it will also calculate the line loss.

■ This may be the most simple calculation to make graphically with a Smith Chart.[C] Recall that if the Z is just resistive (X=0), the SWR is either Z_0/Z or Z/Z_0, depending on whether the Z is lower or higher than the Z_0. Recall also that a circle on a Smith Chart represents constant SWR. Thus if you enter the Z on the Smith Chart and draw a circle centered on the chart center, it will show the transformed Z for any length of line. Either point at which the circle crosses the resistive axis can be

Table B

Impedance of Loads that Result in Different SWRs.

For Ideal 50 Ω Coaxial Cable

R (Ω)	X (Ω)	SWR
50	0	1:1
25	0	2:1
100	0	2:1
50	±35	2:1
30	±18	2:1
16.7	0	3:1
150	0	3:1
50	±58	3:1
30	±40	3:1
5	0	10:1
500	0	10:1
50	±142	10:1
250	±250	10:1

used to calculate the SWR as described above.

■ If you have neither computer nor Smith Chart, you can compute the SWR directly. This can be found, for example, in a book I had as a text many years ago, a classic by the late John Kraus, W8JK, *Antennas*. In the first edition it is in the appendix on page 507. The calculation is done in two steps:

1. Find the voltage reflection coefficient σ:
$$\sigma = (Z-Z_0)/(Z+Z_0)$$
Note that the Z is a complex number, so the calculation is a bit tedious.
2. Find the SWR = $(1 + |\sigma|) / (1 - |\sigma|)$
where |σ| indicates the magnitude of the complex reflection coefficient, σ, found in step 1.

Notes
[A] W. Maxwell, W2DU, *Reflections*, check his Web site for information on availability of the latest edition at **w2du.com**.
[B] R. D. Straw, Editor, *The ARRL Antenna Book,* 21st Edition. Available from your ARRL dealer or the ARRL Bookstore, ARRL order no. 9876. Telephone 860-594-0355, or toll-free in the US 888-277-5289; **www.arrl.org/shop; pubsales@arrl.org**.
[C] Paper copies of 50 Ω Smith Charts are available from your ARRL dealer or the ARRL Bookstore, ARRL order no. 1341. Telephone 860-594-0355, or toll-free in the US 888-277-5289; **www.arrl.org/shop; pubsales@arrl.org**.

is usable on any band — you just crank until you are within range. It may even be helpful for upper body development.

The capacitor can be a single, or multiple section type or a combination of a variable and fixed capacitors. In my tuner, the switch that moves the capacitor from one end of the inductor to the other has additional positions that switch in fixed capacitors in parallel to extend the tuning range. The fixed and variable combination allows somewhat finer tuning, but in multiple steps. A larger variable with a multi-turn vernier dial may be equivalent, and may be quicker to adjust.

An advantage of the L-network tuner is that there is only a single combination of L and C that will match a given load. As noted below, some tuners can offer more than one, but only one is optimum.

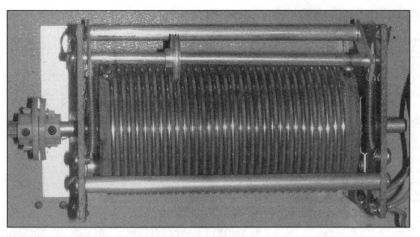

Figure 3-5 — Close up of a rotary inductor.

Pi- and T-Network Tuner Controls

Pi- and T-network tuners have three tuning controls — usually one inductor and two capacitors. Pi-network tuners that started out in the age of vacuum tube transmitters with pi-network output circuits often are built with similar components and are thus bandswitched as in the Drake MN-2000 tuner shown in **Figure 3-6**. In this tuner, the bandswitch sets the inductance to a preset coil tap for the middle of the expected range and the capacitors on both ends are used to provide the closest match. This configuration can be useful, but generally has less tuning range than those with adjustable or switched inductors in small increments.

Note that a pi-network tuner set to minimum capacitance on either of the capacitors essentially becomes an L-network tuner, with the high or low impedance determination dependent on which capacitor is set to around zero.

With either the pi- or T-network tuners, sometimes multiple very different settings can be found that will tune a particular load. In general, a setting with the minimum inductance is more efficient since the wire resistance of the inductor can dissipate power.

Tuned Transformer Tuner Controls

The tuned transformer is essentially the same as an output circuit from an earlier, before the pi-network, kind of transmitter. It typically has a balanced tuned circuit designed to resonate on a particular band (there weren't as many back then) using a fixed inductor and variable capacitor. The typically balanced transmission line was tapped symmetrically on the coil — close to the center for low impedance loads, close to the ends for high impedance loads. Small clips were generally used to provide load connection points. Very low impedance loads were connected in series with the center of the inductor.

Any reactance in the load would detune the tuned circuit that would then be readjusted by retuning the variable capacitor. The usual transmitter side connection was a link of a few turns that could be mechanically moved in and out of the center of the coil to provide adjustable coupling.

It was actually simpler to adjust than to describe. Once the tap points were located for a particular band using the usual single antenna, the clips were fixed in place, and this became just one more coil to be changed while changing frequencies. Both transmitters and receivers of the pre WW2 era often had plug-in coils that required changing each time a band change was desired.

The 1950s era E. F. Johnson *Matchbox* antenna tuner (see **Figure 3-7**) was a radical design change to the tuner transformer type of tuner. This was the era in which transmitters and receivers were generally bandswitched and the Matchbox was an effort to make antenna tuning just as easy. What made the matchbox unique was a patented differential capacitor design that allowed a variable capacitance to be made of two capacitors — one that increased and one that decreased as it was rotated.

A pair of these were placed across the tuner resonant circuit allowing the transmission lines in the middle of each to be tapped across the resonant circuit using capacitive "taps" instead of the previous inductive taps. This allowed a continuously adjustable impedance setting to be made from the front panel. The bandswitching allowed bands to be changed without changing coils. This was very popular at the time, and they are still popular today. They do have some limitations, principally that they only work on the amateur bands of that day, not 30, 17 and 12 meters — although they may

Figure 3-6 — 1970's vintage bandswitched pi-network tuner.

**Figure 3-7 —
1950's vintage
E. F. Johnson
Matchbox
antenna tuner.**

drive some loads on the higher bands by setting to an adjacent band.

Antenna Tuner Metering

Many antenna tuners include metering, either directional power meters or an SWR bridge. These can be used to monitor progress while adjusting the antenna tuner — either for minimum reflected power, or for minimum SWR. Arguably, this is somewhat redundant if the connected radio transmitter also has SWR or reflected power measurement capability, although some meters in tuners may be more sensitive or easy to read.

While there is certainly no harm in having redundant metering, if your radio meter is easily visible from the antenna tuner location, and has

sufficient sensitivity to allow proper tuning, there isn't much benefit in my opinion. The early transceivers, and especially pre-transceiver transmitters, did not generally include that function, perhaps explaining why most tuner manufacturers still provide them. For most users with metering in the transmitter, transmission line current meters on the output side of the tuner would actually be more useful. To my knowledge, alas, no tuner manufacturers now include these.[1,2]

Tuner Limitations

All tuners are composed of combinations of inductors and capacitors in various combinations. Since the

[1]Notes appear on page 9.

impedance at a high SWR can vary widely, the tuner needs to have a wide range of values in order to be able to accommodate all possibilities at every frequency within its range. It is generally the case that the lower the frequency, the more inductance and capacitance will be required. Thus the maximum available inductance and capacitance, generally determines the low frequency limit of operation.

In the case of high power tuners with large components, it is not unusual for tuners that cover down to 160 meters (1.8 MHz) to be in larger enclosures simply because the size of the components is larger. In a similar way, it is the minimum capacitance and inductance that sets the high frequency limit. In this case, one must often look beyond the specified values of the components themselves and look to the stray capacitance of wires and component frames to the cabinet, as well as the inductance of connecting wires between components. Some tuners have trouble matching loads on 10 meters (28 to 29.7 MHz in the US) that would be easy to match at lower frequencies for this reason.

Increasing power with high SWR can result in very high currents and voltages within the tuner, requiring large components for high power tuners. The large components, in addition to making the box much bigger, also make the control of stray inductance and capacitance more of a challenge for the designer.

Where are the Knobs on an Automatic Antenna Tuner?

Automatic antenna tuners don't generally have tuning knobs. Instead, they have a microcontroller that monitors SWR or reflected power and uses an algorithm to step through allowable values of L and C until a match is found. Any of the tuner topologies in Figure 3-3 could be used in an automatic tuner with an appropriate control mechanism.

Some automatic tuners use rotating variable capacitors and rotary inductors, just as in many manual tuners. In fact some are adaptations of manual tuners with servo motors and controllers added on as an additional physical and logical layer.

I do think it is safe to say, however, that the majority of auto tuners use a set of discrete components instead of variable ones. A range of inductance is provided by using relays to switch different sizes in series to reach the desired value. Similarly, a range of capacitance can be provided by having multiple capacitors switched in parallel. By having values available in a series such as 1, 2, 4, 8, 16, 32, 64, 128, 256 for example, any value from 1 to 511 (either pF or µH) can be obtained in steps of 1 unit. Thus any needed resolution and range can be easily provided.

While such switching, if done manually with toggle switches, might make us go over the top, it's duck soup for a microprocessor. The hard part may be defining a computer algorithm that can quickly find the right values without trying all combinations. Fortunately, that just needs to be done once and is provided "free" with the tuner. Most auto tuners can find a suitable match within a defined threshold, often 1.5:1, within a few seconds with no additional information about the antenna being tuned.

Many auto tuners have the capability to memorize the appropriate settings for a particular load once it's found. There are two approaches to this, both can be quite successful:

Memory stored by frequency. Perhaps most commonly found in tuners is the storage of tuning data based on frequency. Of course, this requires that the tuner measure the frequency before it can tune.[3] Most tuners have a number of frequency "bins" of a certain bandwidth, for example perhaps 25 kHz. If the frequency is within that bin, the last successful setting from a frequency within that bin will be used. If it doesn't meet the threshold, the tuner will start tuning over.

Obviously, the smaller the bin, the more successful the tune is likely to be, assuming the same antenna is used. On the other hand, this depends on previous operation within the bin, so it takes longer to accumulate data for all bins. Most tuners seem to have it about right, in terms of trade off.

Memory stored by past success. A different approach is to just keep track of the last number of successful tuner settings, independent of frequency. Let's say the tuner remembers the last 100 successful tuner settings. It just very quickly tries all those before it initiates its regular tuning algorithm. It is quite likely that recent conditions will be repeated. This approach is particularly advantageous for a single port tuner that is switched between multiple antennas making multiple successful tuner settings appropriate within a single frequency bin. Of course an advantage for the manufacturer is that the tuner doesn't need to measure or otherwise determine transmitting frequency.

What's the Best Tuner for You?

The best tuner for a particular application will depend largely depend on your antenna system and operational needs. Automatic antenna tuners inside transceivers are convenient and don't require extra space or wiring. Check the specs carefully, many do not cover a wide impedance range (many are spec'd at 3:1, although some may do better than spec). Interestingly, the internal tuners from Elecraft, FlexRadio and Ten-Tec do provide wide range (to 10:1 SWR) tuning, perhaps others will follow in this direction. The other disadvantage of internal tuners is that you will need a tuner with a higher power rating if you use, or consider using a linear amplifier. A high power tuner will work fine at low power, if the linear is in your plans.

Manual Tuners often offer antenna switching and control functions, not present in many auto tuners. Manual tuners also often provide continuous tuning to allow setting the controls for an exact 1:1 SWR, although that doesn't really provide a significant benefit.

Automatic tuners have a number of advantages and not many disadvantages. Some can be operated remotely at or near the antenna to reduce system losses. Either of the memory tuner types can reduce the tuning time for previously encountered antennas from a few seconds to a few tenths of seconds. Arguably either is significantly quicker to get into operation than a manual tuner, even with recorded dial settings.

The rest of the book will explore these issues in more detail.

Notes
[1] E. Nichols, KL7AJ, "Keeping Current with Antenna Performance," *QST*, Feb 2009, pp 34-36.
[2] P. Danzer, N1II, "A Simple Transformer to Measure Your Antenna Current," *QST*, Sep 2009, p 35.
[3] Internal, or brand specific tuners have the advantage that the frequency information can be made instantly available from the radio circuitry.

Review Questions

3-1 What are two reasons to provide a matched, or nearly matched, load to a transmitter?

3-2 What is the SWR of a 50 Ω cable with a 500 Ω resistive load? How about a 500 Ω transmission line with a 50 Ω resistive load?

3-3 If a 100 W output transmitter is connected to a lossless antenna system with a 3:1 SWR and it can deliver its full power, how much power reaches the antenna? How much power is reflected from the load?

Chapter 4

Tuning an Antenna Tuner

Tuning controls of three manual tuners. On top, a 100 W Pi-network, in the middle a 1500 W L network tuner and on the bottom a bandswitched 1000 W Pi-network tuner.

Contents

By now we, hopefully, know what an antenna tuner is, and why it may be a good idea. The next question should be "how do we work it?" The answer to this depends a bit on the type of tuner and your configuration. In all cases, the most important rule is: *Don't interfere with other users of the band!* This is an issue because all types of tuners require the transmission of RF for at least the final adjustment.

This is because tuning is considered complete only if the SWR is close to 1:1, and it takes a signal to be able to measure SWR. Even if the signal is of a reduced amplitude, people have been known to make worldwide contacts with transmitters running less than 1 W, so don't assume a low powered TUNE signal won't go anywhere.

If you are worried about loosing track of the current frequency that has a particularly desirable station; just put it in memory, tune off the frequency, adjust the tuner and, when tuning is complete, recall the desired frequency from the memory. You should be good to go, and you won't ruin it for someone else.

Tuning an Automatic Tuner

As its name implies, tuning an automatic tuner should be, well *automatic*. If it's a tuner that is part of the radio, or designed to operate with the radio, there is likely a TUNE button that reduces power, sends a carrier on the desired frequency and then forces the tuner to tune. Many after-market automatic tuners first measure the frequency and try the settings that worked the last time you used that frequency, or one close to it.

If the tuner is one that is not designed to work with the radio, you generally will need to initiate the process in some way. In many cases, if a transmitted RF signal is sent to the tuner it will measure the SWR and automatically initiate the tuning process if it needs to. There are two concerns here — first, many tuners want adjustments to be made at reduced power to avoid burning relay contacts — second, reduced power should also be used during tuning to avoid potential transmitter damage from trying to feed a mismatched load, as well as to reduce interference to others.

You will need to find a way to easily reduce power for tuning. Some radios do exactly that with a TUNE button. On my transceiver, I have such a button and a menu selection allows me to set the tune power to any level I want. Pushing the TUNE button sends a reduced carrier out of the transmitter until I push it again. This button is also useful to start tuning a linear amplifier. If you don't have a TUNE button, you may need to manually reduce power and then hit a key to send a signal. Note that I said *key*, as in radiotelegraph mode. Hitting the push-to-talk button on a SSB voice transmitter will switch to transmit, but not put out a signal until you start talking — so that doesn't work well for this application. If your transmitter supports AM voice, it will usually put out a carrier of about 25% of full PEP when keyed, so that is a possibility as well, although that is usually somewhat more power than desired.[1]

[1]Transmitters such as the early R. L. Drake vacuum tube series use controlled carrier in AM mode and may not put out a carrier without speech.

Tuning a Manual Tuner

To tune a manual tuner, you can actually start with the transmitter turned off. First look at the instruction manual and see if it provides suggested settings for each band. While your actual settings will be somewhat different, since you will have a different impedance on each band, they should make a good starting point. Hopefully the controls on your tuner have calibration marks on each control, if not, imagine an analog clock face on each control.

Next, practice tuning your tuner into a dummy load. Even though the tuner usually isn't needed to match the 50 Ω dummy load to the transmitter, if the tuner is in line, the tuner will require just as careful adjustments to tune into that load. Try the tuner on each band and record the settings.

Adjusting a Manual Tuner

Most manual antenna tuners have three controls. If it's a Pi- or T-network, they will all be adjustable inductors or capacitors, usually one of the former and two of the latter. An L-network will just have one of each but will usually have a switch to move the variable capacitor between the input and output side of the inductor as shown in Figure 3-3 in Chapter 3. Because the three controls interact to some degree, finding the right settings can be arduous, can stress the transmitter and can also cause interference to others as you try to find the right settings, hence the recorded table. I provide the following suggestions.

•Many antenna tuner instruction manuals have tables of typical values for each band. Use these as a starting point.

•Practice tuning your antenna tuner into a dummy load, as discussed above.

•First tune as close as you can using the receiver as an indicator. If there are signals on the band, adjust for maximum S-meter indication. If

there are no signals adjust for loudest band noise or meter indication.

•If you have an antenna analyzer, use it instead of the radio to find settings that offer a matched load to the radio port as shown in **Figure 4-1**.

•If you can't quite get to a 1:1 SWR, shift one of the controls off its minimum position and adjust the other one (or two) for minimum. If the result is better, move the first control a bit more in the same direction. Repeat until it starts to get worse. If it's still not satisfactory, repeat the procedure with a different control.

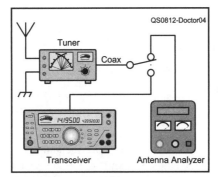

Figure 4-1 — Using an antenna analyzer to adjust your antenna tuner reduces both stress to your radio and interference to other users of the band. The coax switch shown can be used to switch the output of the antenna tuner to either the radio or the antenna analyzer.

•If there are multiple settings yielding a match, as there will likely be with T- and Pi-network tuners, select the one with minimum inductance — it will be more efficient because inductors tend to have more loss than air variable capacitors. The following example illustrates the point.

A fairly typical "random" length of wire likely to be matched with an antenna tuner would be 57.5 feet long fed against ground. This would have an impedance of 25.6 Ω resistive in series with 100 Ω capacitive reactance at 3.7 MHz — a 10:1 SWR, just within the design range of most wide range tuners. A low-pass L-network tuner will just have a single value of L and C that would mach this impedance. It would be, according to *TLW* software (discussed later in detail), 5.29 μH and 1000 pF. The loss in the L-network tuner would be 0.11 dB or 2.5%.

With a high-pass T-network tuner, there are an infinite number of combinations of tuner components that can result in a satisfactory match. Setting one value requires the other two components each be set to a particular value to obtain a match. As shown in **Table 4-1**, listed by selected value of output capacitor, not all combinations will have the same efficiency. It shows dramatically that by having a

Table 4-1

Examination of High-Pass T-Network Tuner Efficiency as a Function of Tuning: Load 25.6 Ω Resistive in Series with 100 Ω Capacitive at 3.7 MHz.

Capacitor Output (pF)	Intput (pF)	Inductor (μH)	Loss (dB)	Loss (%)
5	9.2	130.6	8.5	85.9
10	12.5	82.1	5.4	71.3
30	25.7	34.4	2.4	41.7
50	37.5	22.5	1.6	29.9
100	63.2	12.8	0.9	18.4
200	102.6	7.8	0.5	11.5
500	171.2	4.7	0.3	6.8
1000	223.2	3.7	0.23	5.2
2000	264	3.2	0.19	4.4
5000	297	2.6	0.17	3.9

Table 4-2

W1ZR Antenna Tuner Settings Table

Antenna Tuner Settings — 100 Ft Dipole (4)

| | | | | | AMP SET | |
FREQ	C	IMPED	L	SWR	Load	Tune
1.8	8.0	L5	4 - 9.9	2.5	0.0	8.0
3.55	5.6	H1	20 - 6.9	12.0	4.0	5.8
3.8	1.0	H1	18 - 1.9	9.8	8.8	4.7
5.3	4.3	H1	12 - 9.5	5.8		
7.0	1.2	H2	6 - 5.0	4.6	7.8	2.7
7.2	8.5	H1	8 - 1.0	5.6		
10.1-.15	8.8	H1	4 - 6.3	4.4		
14.0	2.0	H1	4 - 5.6	4.0	7.0	1.5
14.2	1.3	H1	4 - 6.4	3.7	7.0	1.4
18.068-.168	4.1	H1	2 - 7.7	2.9	7.0	2.0
21.0	3.0	L1	2 - 6.5	3.7	6.2	1.5
21.2	2.6	L1	2 - 6.2	4.3		
21.3	2.5	L1	2 - 6.3	4.5	6.0	1.3
24.890-.990	1.5	H1	1 - 1.8	1.8		
28.0	1.0	L1	3 - 5.4	1.6	5.0	2.0
28.5	1.0	L1	2 - 9.6	2.5	4.5	2.0
29.0	1.0	L1	2 - 6.0	3.6		

Antenna Tuner Settings — Tri-Band (2)

| | | | | | AMP SET | |
FREQ	C	IMPED	L	SWR	Load	Tune
10.1-.15	4.0	L1	9 - 1.3	5		
18.068-.168	3.3	L1	4 - 8.2	5	7	2.0

Antenna Tuner Settings — Ground Plane (3)

| | | | | | AMP SET | |
FREQ	C	IMPED	L	SWR	Load	
3.6	10.0	L1	9 - 1.7	2.3	4	5.8

high inductance value, the loss will be higher than if an inductor with a lower value were used. All combinations will provide a 1:1 match to the transmitter which will happily pump power into the system. While some values would likely not be realizable at 3.7 MHz, the reactances all would be easily employed at 30 MHz. A 1500 W transmitter with the 86% loss of the first entry would dissipate 1290 W in the tuner as heat. The tuner would likely melt before your eyes!

Note that Table 1 indicates that the highest efficiency is with the lowest inductance value — often the case. It also can happen that the high Q of a low inductance solution can result in large circulating currents resulting in additional loss. The best way to be sure is to measure the relative current going from the tuner to the antenna. The solution with the highest current will be the most efficient.

The actual value of the current isn't usually significant since the antenna impedance is unknown. For any given antenna on a given frequency, what is important is that you have the solution that provides the most current towards the antenna with the transmitter operating into its design load and within ratings. Unfortunately, I am not aware of any tuners now available that provide for the measurement of antenna current. RF ammeters are available on the surplus market and one is available from MFJ. Alternately, a fairly simple antenna current transformer project article in *QST* described how to make your own. It is reproduced in the following sidebar.

Once you have a match, reduce the inductance, retune the capacitors, and see if you can still obtain a match with an even higher current. Once you have the settings for a particular antenna, you won't need to measure the current again unless something

changes in the system.

•Record your data! All manual antenna tuners I've seen have calibrated scales on their front panel for each control. As soon as you have a match, write down the settings you found for future reference and use them for a starting point next time. I find that having a set of dial readings for at least the phone and CW portions of the band is useful. **Table 4-2** is the actual table that I use at my station. Note that there are separate table segments for three different antennas. The fourth position is connected to a dummy load for testing and amplifier adjustment purposes.

The Controls in My Table

Since there's a bit more here than you might need, let me explain the columns I have included in my chart. The tuner I use is an early Ten-Tec 238 with front panel layout shown in the chapter title (center) figure. This is a 1.5 kW rated L-network tuner that provides four antenna connection ports, one of which (# 4) can be set up for either a balanced or unbalanced load using an internal balun on the output side.

• FREQ is the approximate frequency that I made the adjustment for.

•C is the approximate setting of the variable capacitor dial. It has 10 divisions, but I "eyeballed" how far between the marks the setting was to get the tenths position.

•IMPED is a switch that can set the configuration for high (H) or low (L) impedance and has five fixed capacitor settings for each, hence the numbers 1 through 5, in addition to the letter.

•L is the setting for the variable inductor. The inductor setting has two numbers because it is a multiple turn rotary inductor. The first number is the value of the TURNS scale, while the second is the knob setting from the skirt on the knob.[2]

[2]Current models of this tuner have an improved drive for the rotary inductor that provides a single reading for the L value.

• SWR is the SWR measured with the tuner bypassed. This doesn't play a part in the tuning, but is useful as a check to make sure the antenna hasn't changed or fallen down since it was installed. The tuner will just as happily tune the antenna if it breaks and falls down, but the signal won't go as far.

• The two AMP SET adjustments are for my linear amplifier tuning controls. They share the spreadsheet because, as with the antenna tuner, if I change bands or modes, they need adjustment. These columns save having an additional piece of paper on the operating desk. If you don't have a linear amplifier you don't need these.

Your tuner may have different control labels, and you may not want to include all my data, however, it should give you a starting point for your own record keeping. I maintain my records on a PC spreadsheet, although any convenient medium can be used. A small set of data might fit on a 3 × 5 (or perhaps 5 × 7) inch file card. The spreadsheet has the advantage that it can be easily updated as antennas are changed or added. In my experience, amateur stations are never quite done!

A Simple Transformer to Measure Your Antenna Current

SWR doesn't give you the whole story — you need an RF current meter.

Paul Danzer, N1II

Figure 1 — View of the transformer and simple circuitry that make up the relative RF current meter.

In a recent *QST* article, Eric Nichols, KL7AJ, presented a good idea — monitoring the RF current into your antenna system to insure optimum tuning.[1] Actually, it was the second time it was mentioned to me — George Peters, K1EHW, suggested the same thing to me several months before. At the end of Eric's article, he proposed using a current transformer to do the monitoring.

Making a Current Transformer

This could be as simple as a turn of wire through a ferrite core and several turns of wire around the core to form a transformer.[2] The output of the transformer would be proportional to the current through the wire.

Making it Happen

This seemed simple enough, and the result of one hour's work is shown in Figure 1. The core used was a T37-6. T37 designates the size (0.37 inches OD), picked so the insulated center conductor of RG-58 (or RG-59) would fit comfortably through the core center. The –6 designation relates to the frequency application of the ferrite mix, in this case 2 to 50 MHz.

Searching the ARRL suppliers' data base, it appears that Alstar Magnetics offers this core; an alternate would be a Palomar F37 with mix 61. There is no criticality here — if you want to try it, strip a core from any old source — perhaps from a junked PC power supply or computer cable. It may not be the most efficient RF transformer ever built, but if it works it will do the job.

Wrap 20 turns of 24 gauge enameled wire as the transformer secondary. The secondary is connected to half wave rectifier consisting of a silicon diode (1N914), a 10 kΩ resistor as the load and a 0.1 µF capacitor as a filter (see Figure 2). A high-impedance voltmeter (the $10 variety) is connected to the two pin jacks to serve as an indicator.

The unit shown was tested with a 100 W transmitter on all bands from 80 through 10 meters. Performance across each band was relatively uniform, considering the probable variation of SWR and power though the feed line as the frequency was varied.

Hook up the rest of the circuit as shown in Figure 2 and connect a meter to the terminals.

What we Have

The object here was not to get an exact measure of the antenna current. What I wanted was a relative measure, so I could see if anything was going wrong, or use it as a way to adjust my antenna tuner for the maximum signal to the antenna. Commercial stations use a current meter, mounted at the connection of the feed line to the antenna, to monitor output. Since they know the antenna impedance and their meters are calibrated, they can determine precise power into the antenna.

If you enjoy low power (QRP, typically 5 W or less) or very low power (QRPP, less than 1 W) operation, more turns may be needed and can easily be added.[3] Similarly, if your meter does not have enough sensitivity, more turns may be called for. If after assembly the core is not firmly in place, held by the friction of the secondary on the primary wire, a drop of glue can be used to secure it all together.

Putting it to Use

The current meter consumes a miniscule fraction of the output power, so, can be left in the line, or removed when not in use. You may even find a meter case and a surplus meter at a hamfest that will work with it to give continuous indication without tying up your bench meter. I suggest writing the relative current indication for each band in your log. Later, if something seems amiss, it is then an easy job to compare your readings to the recorded ones to find out if the problem is in your antenna system.

Notes

1. E. Nichols, KL7AJ, "Keeping Current with Antenna Performance," *QST*, Feb 2009, pp 34-36.
2. Each pass through the center of a toroid counts as a full turn.
3. Low power operators may obtain better results using a germanium diode, such as a 1N34, in place of the silicon diode due to its lower forward voltage drop.

ARRL Member Paul Danzer, N1II, was first licensed in 1953, and now holds an Amateur Extra class license. Paul has been operating 40 meter CW almost constantly since he first started. He uses his years of experience as an electronic engineer to design and build small, one-night ham radio projects. Currently he is a Professor of Computer Science at Housatonic Community College in Connecticut. He can be reached at **n1ii@arrl.net**.

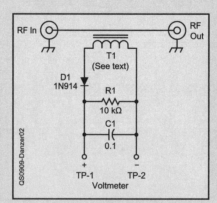

Figure 2 — Schematic diagram of the relative RF current meter. Nothing about the circuit is critical. See text for parts information.

From September 2009 QST © ARRL

Review Questions

4-1 Why is it important to listen to the operating frequency before you start the tuning process?

4-2 Why is it a good idea to manually initiate tuning with your auto-tuner before transmitting on a new frequency at full power?

4-3 If there are more than one set of tuner settings that provide a 1:1 SWR, which should you choose?

Chapter 5

The Internal Tuner — How Does it Help?

The Yaesu FT-2000 transceiver, one of many modern transceivers equipped with an automatic internal antenna tuner.

Contents

So far, our discussions about antenna tuners have made it appear that they are a separate device that is inserted between a transceiver and an antenna system. While that's often true, we should also consider the case of a transceiver that has an internal, almost always automatic, antenna tuner.

The idea of an automatic antenna tuner is that it can sense the SWR and adjust the tuner to minimize it. This is most commonly accomplished by a configuration consisting of a collection of inductors and capacitors that can be switched in or out of a matching network until the lowest SWR is obtained. A few automatic tuners actually rotate the shaft of a variable capacitor using an electric motor as the driving element.

The Flavors of Internal Tuners

Some transceivers offer an internal tuner as an extra cost option, in many cases one that can be added if needed. In other cases, the transceiver with tuner is essentially a separate model that has to be specified at the time of purchase. Other transceiver lines come only with or only without an internal tuner. Thus, if you're in the process of deciding on your next (or first) transceiver it's good to think carefully about your requirements before you make a decision. **Figures 5-1 – 5-3** illustrate radios with some of the choices.

Tuner Impedance Range

As noted previously, all antenna tuners have limits on the range of impedances that they can transform to the desired load — almost always 50 Ω. In many cases the range of values is dependent on the frequency, often narrower on 6 meters than on the HF bands. Most tuner designs are limited on the low frequency end by the maximum values of the inductors and capacitors, and on the high frequency end by their minimum values, often the minimum capacitance of the elements to the metal case.

Thus it is often the case that the range of impedance values that the tuner is able to match is greater in the middle of the range than on the ends — typically 80 or 160 meters on the low end and 10 or 6 meters on the high end. Most manufacturers provide a single specification such as "tunes SWR at least 10:1" or "matches from 5 to 500 Ω." Note that the latter specification is not as general as the first — does it mean it only matches

Figure 5-1 — The Elecraft K-3 is an entirely modular design, including the option of a wide-range internal antenna tuner.

Figure 5-2 — The ICOM IC-7600 is only available with a built in antenna tuner.

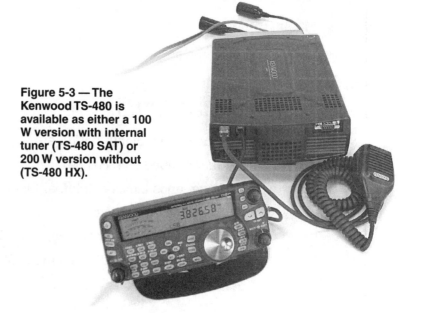

Figure 5-3 — The Kenwood TS-480 is available as either a 100 W version with internal tuner (TS-480 SAT) or 200 W version without (TS-480 HX).

resistive loads? Probably not, since it would be hard to design a tuner that just did that, nor would it be very useful. I tend to think that both ratings actually mean the same 10:1 SWR.

If they deliver on their promise, that would mean that they would actually tune the 10:1 range on the highest and lowest bands, and actually tune a wider range in the middle — and many seem to do just that.

Impedance Limits of Internal Tuners

While most external tuners have rating similar to the 10:1 discussed above, many transceivers have internal tuners rated at a 3:1, or 16.5 to 150 Ω tuning range. This seems to be particularly true of the radios provided by the large Japanese companies — ICOM, Kenwood and Yaesu. In contrast, the US made HF transceivers, Elecraft, FlexRadio and Ten-Tec, offer internal tuners specified to tune a 10:1 range.

The tuners with a 3:1 range are intended to deal with a matched antenna operated somewhat away from its design frequency. A look at the SWR plots in Chapter 2 provides the idea. While a 3:1 range will easily cover a 40 meter dipole across the whole band, it will only cover about 300 kHz of the 500 kHz width of 80 meters with a standard 80 meter wire dipole (see Figure 2-7).

The tuners with a tuning range of 10:1 or greater are what I call *wide range* tuners. These tuners can not only deal with an 80 meter dipole across the whole band, but can be used to match a whole spectrum of antenna types ranging from random, non resonant, wires to dipoles fed on multiple bands and exotic high gain antennas such as V beams or rhombics.

That Coax Connector

All current internal tuners terminate on the back of the radio in a coax connector, just as do radios without a tuner. This is a signal that they are intended to drive into coax fed *unbalanced* antenna systems. We will discuss the various benefits of balanced and unbalanced transmission lines a bit later, however, it is worth pointing out that many external tuners are set up to drive either. If your antenna system is balanced, you will need to make the transition from coax to balanced line outside the radio, tending to reduce the "all in one box" benefit of the internal tuner.

Coax Loss — If Things Seem Too Good to Be True...

It is tempting to try to use the antenna tuner to "force fit" an antenna to work on a band other than the one it's designed for. This can often appear to work, but appearances can be deceiving. Let's take one example.

Say you have a 20 meter dipole fed with 100 feet of RG-58 coaxial cable. The antenna works very well on 20 meters, and requires just a bit of trimming with the tuner for proper operation. So far so good.

All of a sudden sunspots reappear after years of absence and 10 meters is wide open with great signals world wide (sooner or later it's bound to happen). You have no antenna for 10 meters, so try using your 20 meter dipole. Wonder of wonders, it actually tunes with the internal tuner — a perfect match! You hear your neighbors working distant stations right and left, but no one hears you — what's the story?

This is an interesting case that provides a cautionary tale, as well as outlines one of the challenges of designing multiband antennas. On 20 meters, our dipole (depending on height) will have an SWR of around 1:1. The 100 feet of RG-58 coax will have a loss of about 37% (less than 2 dB), not noticeable in most cases, and all will be fine.[1]

Move to 10 meters and the 20 meter dipole will no longer provide a good match. In fact, my model indicates that its impedance will be 3836 Ω resistive in series with 790 Ω capacitive reactance — an SWR of 81:1! The high SWR increases the loss of the transmission line to about 15 dB. That means that of our 100 W, only 3.1 W will reach the antenna — that explains why we aren't being heard as well as our neighbors!

The perhaps more interesting aspect of this is that the power reflected by the mismatched antenna also is reduced by 15 dB on its way back to the tuner. Because of this, the tuner only sees an SWR at the bottom of the cable of about 3:1 and will happily adjust for a match. Thus the radio is happily transmitting, but 97% of its power output is heating up the transmission line.

What Else is Going to be in Your Station?

Another consideration as to whether an internal tuner will be your best choice is whether you have, or expect to have, a linear amplifier following your transceiver. For some types of operation, being able to select whether you transmit 100 or 1500 W can make a big difference.

If you have a linear amplifier and need a tuner, you will need an antenna tuner on the output side of your linear. A tuner in your transceiver can adjust for a mismatch in the input side of the amplifier (rarely needed), but can't help with tuning the antenna system. That has to be done at the output of the amplifier — and at the higher power level. If the amplifier is turned off, the radio's tuner can be used to match the antenna, but you will want to disable it when you switch to high power.

Thus, if you have or expect to have, a linear amplifier as a part of your station; you may want to consider a transceiver without a tuner and instead purchase a tuner with a power rating that can handle your linear. Note that this is mostly a monetary statement, since there is no harm in having the additional tuner in your transceiver. It can be turned off if you don't need it. I actually have one in my transceiver and another following the linear. I find the transceiver's internal tuner handy when I take my transceiver on vacation and am forced to use "antennas of opportunity."

[1]We will use decibels (dB) to express gain and loss ratios throughout the book. If you need a refresher on the topic, please see Appendix A.

Review Questions

5-1 What are some of the advantages of an internal antenna tuner in a transceiver?

5-2 What kind of antennas can be tuned with a tuner that can tune an SWR of 3:1?

5-3 Why isn't an antenna that can be tuned with an internal tuner always effective?

Chapter 6

An External Tuner at the Radio

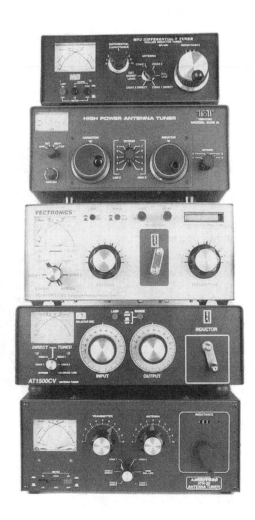

Five high power (1 kW or higher rating) manual tuners, one choice for an external tuner to place near the transceiver

Contents

In place of an antenna tuner that is built into the transceiver, another option is to have one next to the radio. Note that this is the functional equivalent of an internal tuner, and shares the potential problem of appearing to work well with an inappropriate antenna, as described in the previous chapter.

There are many available choices for such a device, including automatic tuners from some radio manufacturers that integrate directly with radio controls. There are others from after market manufacturers that offer additional features and, in some cases, are less expensive than internal tuners. While you do have to have an extra box on or near your radio, external tuners may offer some significant advantages:

• As discussed in Chapter 3, they can have a wider tuning range than many internal tuners.

• If you think you may want to add (or if you have) a high powered linear amplifier, you can select a tuner compatible with the higher power.

• Some external tuners offer both balanced and unbalanced outputs.

• Some external tuners offer multiple switched connections so different antennas can be quickly brought on line.

• If you have multiple radios, they can be switched to the tuner input so only one tuner is needed.

Automatic versus Manual Tuners

The first decision you will be faced with if you want an external tuner is whether you prefer an automatic or a manual one. As the name implies, an automatic antenna tuner finds the optimum, or near optimum, settings by itself. The manual tuner usually has three controls that require adjustment to obtain the best match.

In the past, automatic tuners were not available at high power levels, so those with high powered stations had no choice but to use manual tuners. That is no longer the case, as automatic tuners are available at all legal amateur power levels (See **Figure 6-1**). Over the years, the ARRL has tested many manual and automatic tuners as part of *QST* product reviews. I was surprised to find that to our level of measurement precision, there was not a big difference in efficiency between tuners in the two groups. Still, there are some benefits to manual tuners

Figure 6-1 — High power (1 kW or greater) automatic antenna tuners from Palstar, LDG and MFJ).

and many amateurs are happy with the results they receive.

Automatic Antenna Tuners

To operate an automatic, you just feed it some power, hit a TUNE button and listen and watch while it finds satisfactory settings. Many tuners can do this in tens of seconds the first time and often remember the settings so the next time it takes just a few seconds or less for that antenna at that frequency.

In my experience there's not a lot not to like about an automatic antenna tuner. I have a number of them for particular applications, although I still use a manual tuner for my main station tuner. The key is to select a tuner that will operate with your radio — some are radio independent, while some work with the same radio controls that would operate one from the manufacturer of the radio.

One issue with some automatic tuners is just what happens if they sense a mismatch as you operate. Most automatic tuners are rated to tune at reduced power to avoid excessive arcing at relay contacts. If you change frequency or even if the wind blows your antenna around and the tuner starts tuning, the results could be dramatic. Some allow disabling the auto tune function once you have it tuned, others automatically cut back on power. In my opinion, it's better to be able to take control yourself.

Manual Antenna Tuners

Manual tuners do often provide an additional level of control capability. Some have switch selectable outputs for multiple balanced and unbalanced antenna connections. One can be dedicated to a dummy load, if you don't (yet) have enough antenna connections to fill up the jacks. Manual tuners often provide SWR and power metering independent of that of the radio.

Most automatic tuners tune until they reach what they consider a reasonable match, perhaps 1.5:1. Hopefully it is a value that will allow your radio to operate at full power. The manual tuner let's you set it to whatever threshold you think is best — although if your transmitter can put out full power, it won't make much difference.

Review Questions

6-1 What are three potential benefits of using an external tuner at the radio rather than an internal tuner in the radio?

6-2 What are the benefits of an internal tuner?

6-3 What limitation is common to either internal or external tuners located at the radio?

Chapter 7

Transmission Lines

Transmission lines come in many forms, serving many applications.

Contents

As we have mentioned previously, frequently the antenna and radio are not in exactly the same place. There are some notable exceptions, particularly in portable hand-held systems and various microwave communications and radar systems. In most other cases, optimum performance requires the transmitter and receiver to be at some distance from the antenna. It may also be a matter of combat survival, especially if your enemy is equipped with anti-radiation weaponry designed to home in on a signal. The component that makes the interconnection is called a *transmission line*.

Transmission lines are used in places besides radio systems — for example, power distribution lines are a kind of transmission line, as are telephone wires and cable TV connections. In addition to just transporting signals, transmission lines have some important properties that we will need to understand to allow us to make proper use of them. This section will briefly discuss the key parameters.

Characteristic Impedance

A transmission line generally is composed of two conductors, either parallel wires such as we see on power transmission poles, or one wire surrounding the other as in coaxial cable TV wire. The two configurations are shown in **Figure 7-1**. Either type has a certain inductance and capacitance per unit length and can be modeled as shown in **Figure 7-2**, with the values determined by the physical dimensions of the conductors and the properties of the insulating material between the conductors. If a voltage or signal is applied to such a network, there will be an initial current flow independent of what's on the far end of the line, but based only on the L and C values. The initial current will be the result of the source charging the shunt capacitors through the series inductors and will be the same as if the source were connected to a resistor whose value is equal to the square root of L/C.

If the far end of the line is terminated in a resistive load of the same value, all the power sent down the line will be delivered to the load. This is called a *matched* condition. The impedance determined in this way is called the *characteristic impedance* of the transmission line, and is perhaps the most important parameter associated a transmission line. Common coaxial transmission lines have characteristic impedances (referred to as Z_0) between 35 and 100 Ω, while balanced lines are found in the range of 70 to 600 Ω. What this means to us as radio people, is that if we have an antenna that has an impedance of 50 Ω and a radio transmitter designed to drive a 50 Ω load, we can connect the two with any length of the appropriate 50 Ω coaxial cable and the transmitter will think it is right next to the antenna. The antenna will receive most (see next section) of the transmitted power and all is well with the world!

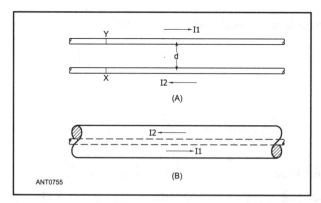

Figure 7-1 — Parallel wire and coaxial transmission lines.

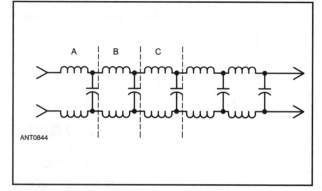

Figure 7-2 — Lumped constant equivalent of an ideal transmission line.

Propagation Velocity

Signals in air dielectric transmission lines propagate at almost the speed of light in air. Other dielectric materials between the conductors cause the signals in transmission lines to slow down just as we observe with light rays traveling through water. In many cases, this is not a matter of concern, since we often only care that the signals get out the other end, however, there are some exceptions.

The velocity can be shown to be reduced by a factor of one over the square root of the relative dielectric constant of the insulating material. Some cable specifications provide the relative velocity as a fraction of the speed of light. If not, and you know the material, most engineering handbooks include tables of properties of materials. For example, polyethylene is a common cable insulating material and has a relative dielectric constant of 2.26. The square root of 2.25 is 1.5, so the propagation velocity in polyethylene insulated coaxial cable is about $3/1.5 \times 10^8$ or 2×10^8 m/sec.

Some applications actually use coaxial cables to provide delayed signals in pulse and other applications. Having a way to accurately predict the delay just by knowing the cable characteristics and measuring the length of the cable can save a lot of lab time.

Attenuation

The ideal transmission line model shown in Figure 7-2 passes all input power to a matched load at the output. A real transmission line also has resistance associated with the wire conductors and some loss of signal due to the nature of the insulating material. As transmission lines are made larger, the resistance is reduced and as the dielectric material gets closer to low-loss air, the losses are reduced. The skin effect causes currents to travel nearer to the surface of the conductors at higher frequencies, and the effective loss thus increases as the frequency is increased.

Figure 7-3 provides some real world examples of the losses as a function of frequency for the most common types of transmission line. Note that the loss increases linearly with length and the values are for a length of 100 feet. Note also that the losses shown are for transmission lines feeding into loads matched to their Z_0. As will be discussed shortly, losses can increase significantly if the line is not matched. The "open wire"

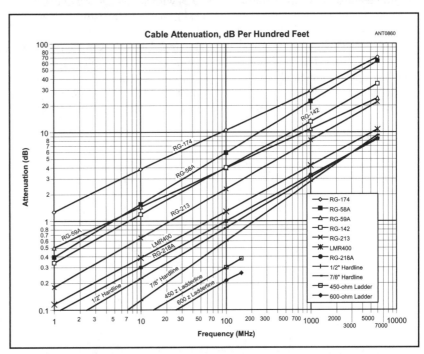

Figure 7-3 — Loss of some typical transmission lines in dB per 100 feet as a function of frequency. The RG-58 transmission lines are 50 Ω polyethelene insulated coaxial cable slightly less than ¼ inch in diameter. The RG-8 through RG-216 are 50 and 70 Ω polyethelene insulated transmission lines with a diameter somewhat less than ½ inch. The "hardline" types have a foam dielectric very near to air.

line shown consists of two parallel wires with air dielectric and infrequent spacers, typically resulting in a Z_0 of around 600 Ω. While the losses of such a line are low, they only work well if spaced from metal objects and lossey material and not coiled up, while coaxial cables have higher loss, all the signal is within the outer conductor and they can be run in conduit, coiled up, placed next to other wires and are therefore much more convenient to work with.

Sometimes a long straight run of open wire line will be transformed to 50 Ω at the ends with coaxial cable used at the antenna and radio ends to take advantage of the benefits of both.

Lines with Unmatched Terminations

In our discussions so far, we have been talking about transmission lines feeding terminations matched to their characteristic impedance. In that case, the voltage-current relationship at the load will reflect the impedance of the load — not the characteristic impedance. Along the line the voltage and current will vary with distance providing a load to the transmitter end that is generally neither that of the far end Z_L, nor the Z_0 of the transmission line. The transmitter load can be calculated knowing the Z_L, the Z_0 and the electrical length of the line as discussed in the sidebar.

The ratio of maximum voltage on

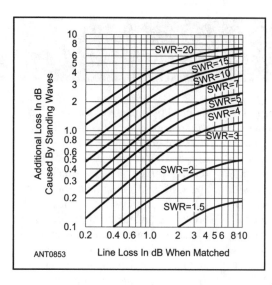

Figure 7-4 — Additional loss of a transmission line when mismatched. This loss needs to be added to the loss in Figure 7-3 for mismatched lines.

the line to minimum voltage on the line is called the *standing wave ratio* or SWR. A matched line has an SWR of 1:1, a 50 Ω line terminated with a 25 or 100 Ω load will have an SWR of 2:1. There are a whole family of complex impedances that will also have a 2:1 SWR, by the way. The computation is easier with resistive loads.

There are some interesting special cases with a mismatched line. The load impedance, resistive or complex, repeats every λ/2, for example. The impedance goes to the opposite extreme in odd multiples of a λ/4. For example our 25 Ω load would get transformed to 100 Ω in λ/4 or ¾ λ transmission line sections and vice

versa. This effect can be used to our advantage if we wish to transform impedances at a specific frequency. In this case, the line is actually acting like a kind of antenna tuner.

A generally less desirable effect of mismatched lines is that the losses increase. This is easy to see, if voltages and currents are higher, we might expect losses to increase as well. **Figure 7-4** provides the additional loss for a mismatched line that needs to be added to the matched loss in Figure 7-3. As is evident, the combination of matched loss and high SWR results in dramatic increases in loss. This is why antenna designs that don't use matched transmission lines often use air-dielectric lines.

What Can We Do to Reduce Transmission Line Loss?

By now you should have a clear understanding of what can happen to a signal if applied to an antenna system through even a relatively short length of coaxial cable that has a high SWR. Depending on the matched loss, length and SWR, much of your signal can disappear before it gets to the antenna.

The insidious aspect of this is that while this is happening, the SWR at the radio with a collocated or internal tuner looks great — a perfect match and easy to get it. Losses are like that — they tend to result in a wide SWR bandwidth, as does a dummy load. Not a good thing if you want to communicate over the air. Fortunately, there are three fairly straightforward approaches to solving this problem:

• Change the antenna to one with either a wide enough bandwidth to cover all frequencies of interest, or one that covers multiple amateur bands with low SWR. This is not a topic for a book on antenna tuners, but is covered in many books on antennas.[1,2]

• Move the antenna tuner to, or close to, the antenna location. This is the subject of Chapter 8, or;

• Use a transmission line that has low enough matched loss so that even a high SWR doesn't result in high losses. This is the subject of Chapter 9.

Notes

[1] J. Hallas, W1ZR, *Basic Antennas — Understanding Practical Antennas and Designs,* Available from your ARRL dealer or the ARRL Book-store, ARRL order no. 9994. Tele-phone 860-594-0355, or toll-free in the US 888-277-5289; **www.arrl.org/arrl-store/**; **pubsales@arrl.org**. See Chapter 11, "Wideband Dipole Arrays;" Chapter 12 "Multiband Dipole Arrays" or Chapter 21 "Log Periodic Dipole Arrays," for example.

[2] R. D. Straw, Editor, *The ARRL Antenna Book,* 21st Edition. Available from your ARRL dealer or the ARRL Bookstore, ARRL order no. 9876. Telephone 860-594-0355, or toll-free in the US 888-277-5289; **www.arrl.org/arrl-store/**; **pubsales@arrl.org**.

Determining the Input Impedance of an Unmatched Transmission Line

The input impedance of a transmission line of any length with any terminating impedance can be determined in a number of different ways.

The most straightforward way is through direct calculation. Unfortunately, this is also perhaps the most time consuming and perhaps most error prone method, at least until you have it set up on a spreadsheet or other program that can handle he hyperbolic function.

My favorite way to determine the input impedance, standing wave ratio (SWR) as well as the line loss, is to use *TLW* (*Transmission Line for Windows*) software that comes with *The ARRL Antenna Book*.[3] The main screen is shown in Figure 7-A performing an analysis of an antenna with a complex load impedance fed through 100 feet of coaxial cable.

The antenna input impedance (74.3 + j16.1) is inserted in the LOAD box. The + j16.1 indicates an inductive reactance with a value of 16.1 Ω at the frequency of interest (10.1 MHz). A –j value would indicate a capacitive reactance, which would be entered with a minus sign. The output impedance through 100 feet of RG-58A 50 Ω coax is provided at the bottom in both rectangular (69.02 – j6.23) and polar coordinates (69.53 @ –5.15°), along with the SWR at line input (1.40:1) and output (1.62:1) as well as line loss (1.661 dB) — both for the matched case (1.555 dB) and the additional loss due to mismatch (0.106 dB). That's about everything I could think to ask, except which pile in the basement has the RG-58A!

A third way to evaluate the input impedance is through a graphical method. A Smith chart, see Figure 7-B, can be used to determine the input impedance of a transmission line. This was very commonly used before the personal computer became ubiquitous. In addition to the accuracy limitations due to the input and output resolution inherent in a chart, the Smith chart assumes that the line is lossless. This may result in significant errors depending on the amount of line loss.

[3] *TLW* is supplied with *The ARRL Antenna Book*, 20th Edition, available from the ARRL Bookstore at **www.arrl.org/ catalog/** order number 9043 — $39.95.

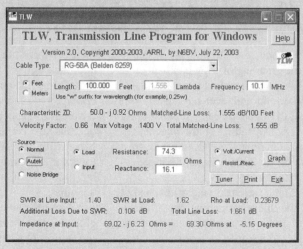

Figure 7-A — The main screen of *TLW* (*Transmission Line for Windows*) software is shown performing an analysis of the condition of the L/D of 10,000 case.

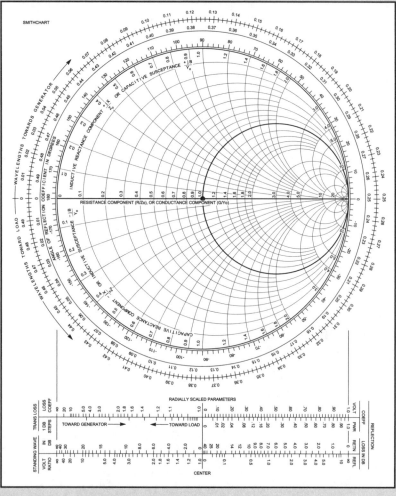

Figure 7-B — A Smith chart used for the graphical determination of the input impedance of a lossless transmission line.

Review Questions

7-1 Describe three reasons it might be desirable to have a transmitter and an antenna in different locations.

7-2 If you want to make a λ/4 section of RG-213 for our 10 MHz system, how long would you make it?

7-3 A 1000 W transmitter at 15 MHz is feeding a matched load through 200 feet of RG-8 transmission line. How much power reaches the antenna? Repeat if the frequency is 150 MHz. Repeat both cases if the antenna has an SWR of 3:1.

Chapter 8

Moving the Tuner to the Back 40

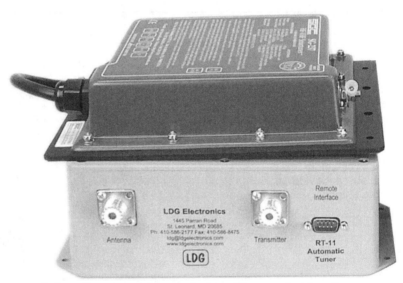

Automatic antenna tuners designed for remote mounting. On top, one from SGC, beneath a model from LDG.

Contents

Some automatic antenna tuners are designed to be mounted remotely, rather than being collocated with the radio. We can take advantage of this in order to minimize losses in the transmission line between the antenna system and the transceiver. With the tuner at the antenna end, the load at the antenna end of the transmission line provides very close to a 1:1 SWR. The line will then have only the matched loss between the radio and the tuner, not the additional loss due to mismatch.

An Example of Using a Remote Tuner to Minimize Loss

Figure 8-1 shows the configuration of a transceiver with a remote automatic antenna tuner at the antenna. Let's assume that the transmission line is RG-58 and that it is 100 feet between the radio and the tuner plus the tuner is connected directly to the feed point of the coax fed antenna.

We will again use the example from Chapter 4 of a 20 meter dipole tuned by the tuner to operate on 10 meters where its impedance will

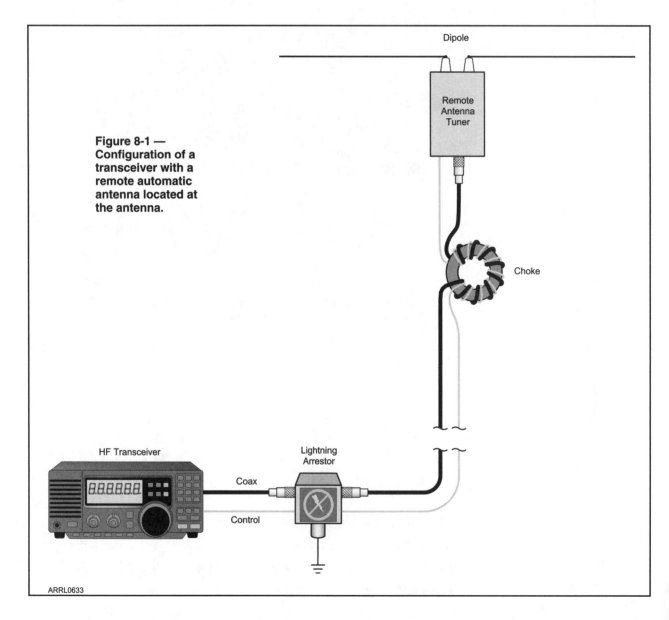

Figure 8-1 — Configuration of a transceiver with a remote automatic antenna located at the antenna.

ARRL0633

Table 8-1

Comparison of System Losses for Remote and Collocated Tuners — RG-58

Loss Element	Tuner at Radio	Remote Tuner Beneath Antenna
Loss in 100' Cable (dB)	14.7	2.9
Percent Power Lost (%)	96.6	48.1
Power to Antenna at 100 W (W)	3.4	51.9

Table 8-2

Comparison of System Losses for Remote and Collocated Tuners — LMR-400

Loss Element	Tuner at Radio	Remote Tuner Beneath Antenna
Loss in 100' Cable (dB)	8.62	0.66
Percent Power Lost (%)	86.3	14.1
Power to Antenna at 100 W (W)	13.7	85.8

be 3836 Ω resistive in series with 790 Ω capacitive reactance — an SWR of 81:1. **Table 8-1** provides the comparison in loss for a 100 W output transceiver, in each case assuming the antenna tuner contributes no loss. While this is slightly optimistic, that loss is usually very small. The result is rather dramatic and illustrates why just hitting the TUNE button on your internal tuner may not provide satisfactory results even if the resulting radio SWR ends up at a perfect match.

Perhaps you will also not be satisfied with moving your tuner to the antenna and still losing almost half your power in the RG-58. The lesson here is that RG-58, while available and relatively inexpensive, is not the best choice for even a 100 foot run at 28 MHz. Of course, it's much worse as you move to VHF, and keep in mind that it effects both transmit and receive signals.

One of the lowest loss flexible coaxial transmission lines that fits the usual UHF coax connectors is Times Wire LMR-400. There are similar cables by other manufacturers. **Table 8-2** repeats the exercise shown in Table 1 with the lower loss cable. Note that while there is measurable loss even for the matched case, it is less than $\frac{1}{10}$ of an S-unit, so hardly noticeable, and much less than the loss for the tuner located at the radio that will result in about a 1.5 S-unit reduction on the receiving station's meter.[1]

[1]Notes appear on page 5.

Not all antenna systems are structured in a way to allow a tuner to be at a feed point. An example might be a dipole suspended between two supports with a transmission line hanging in the middle. In this case, it is tempting to consider a short coax run from the antenna itself to the tuner as shown in **Figure 8-2**. This arrangement may also be necessary if the tuner is not waterproof and requires shelter from the elements.

This is a feasible arrangement; however, while a substantial portion of the loss can be eliminated in this way, the loss in the section between the tuner and the antenna can still be surprisingly high. For example, for the RG-58 case of Table 8-1, a 30 foot run between the antenna and the tuner would have a loss of 4.4 dB, or 64% of the power, leaving only 36 W from your 100 W transmitter to be radiated — if it got to and through the tuner without other losses.

A better way to accomplish this in many cases will be to use a section of the low loss transmission line discussed in Chapter 9 between the antenna and the tuner.

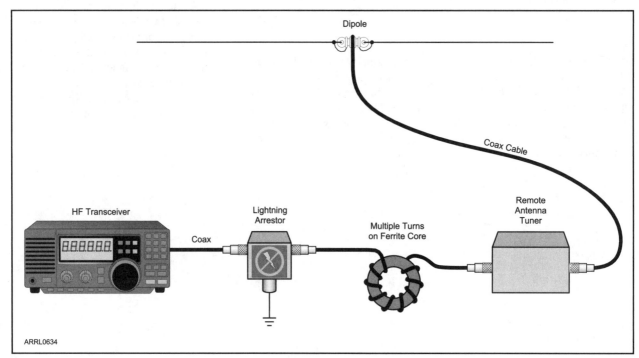

Figure 8-2 — Configuration of a transceiver with a remote automatic antenna located beneath the antenna.

Remote Antenna Tuners — the Downside

The use of a remote antenna tuner has a few disadvantages. I currently use three in various station locations and am quite happy with them in spite of the downsides:

• One remote tuner is located near my main basement station. I share antennas with my spouse (Nancy, W1NCY), who has an upstairs station. With an automatic tuner that can be patched to antennas from the W1ZR main station, she has access to any W1ZR antenna with low loss in the 100 foot coax run to her desktop setup.

• On our sailboat, I use an insulated backstay as an HF antenna. This non-resonant system has a high SWR on all bands and requires a tuner at the feed point to feed it against ground. I have a short lead from a corner under the lazerette beneath the antenna feed with another short lead to the engine block where a ground connection is available. Not only does it work well on all HF bands, but by keeping the radiating portion of the

system in the corner of the boat, I minimize interference between the radio and marine navigation systems.

• I also have a remote tuner in the trunk of my car for my mobile HF system. Typical HF mobile antennas have very narrow SWR bandwidths. By using a remote antenna tuner at the antenna base, I can cover entire bands, or even tune to lower frequency bands than the antenna is designed for. While this sort of operation isn't as efficient as adjusting the antenna itself, it is much easier than making adjustments while driving at highway speeds!

There are a few aspects of remote tuner operation that might be disadvantageous for some. One is the fact that in most such installations the tuner becomes integrated into a particular antenna structure. If we have multiple antennas, each will need its own tuner — a potentially expensive proposition.[2] It also is the case that in addition to providing coaxial cable to the tuner, one must also provide

operating power and sometimes control signals to the tuner. Some tuner manufacturers package the coax, power and control into extension cable assemblies that can be used for this purpose. Another possibility is to use a *bias-T* to insert the power onto the coax cable, sharing it between the two functions.[3]

Notes

[1]The Collins Radio established, now industry standard, S-meter calibration is that S-9 equals 50 µV at the antenna terminals and each S-unit represents a change of 6 dB. To say that not all amateur S-meters follow this standard would be an understatement.

[2]Remotly controlled antenna switches may be used to solve this problem, although commercial units cost as much as some remote 100 W antenna tuners.

[3]S. Ford, WB8IMY, "Short Takes — MFJ-4712 Two-Position Remote Antenna Switch," *QST*, Sep 2006, p 48.

Review Questions

8-1 Why is the quality (loss) of a transmission line more important in the mismatched than the matched case?

8-2 If using an internal tuner in a transceiver, why might the SWR *before* tuning be an important indicator of antenna system efficiency?

8-3 Why is the SWR *before* tuning insignificant if an antenna located tuner can match to the transmission line Z_0?

Chapter 9

Transmission Line Choices for Low Loss

Coaxial cables going up one of the towers at W1AW, the ARRL Headquarters station

Contents

The ideal transmission line accepts the output power (as well as received signal) from its source and delivers it to its destination load without loss. If the characteristic impedance (Z_0) is the same as the source and load impedances, it delivers it with the same ratio of voltage to current. That means, for all practical purposes, the ideal transmission line is invisible to the system. Devices connected to both ends act as if they were collocated, except for the delay in signal arrival time, unimportant except in special circumstances.

Hello Real World!

Unfortunately, ideal transmission lines don't exist, although for many applications we can come remarkably close. The primary issue in most cases is loss. We just don't get as much power to the far end as we put in. There are three primary mechanisms that result in transmission line loss. They are conductor resistance, dielectric loss and leakage or radiation.

Conductor Resistance

Figure 7-1 shows the geometry of the two primary types of transmission line. At (A) is a balanced transmission line, while at (B) we have coaxial cable of the type discussed in the earlier chapters of the book. Both propagate signals down the line as currents with their associated electric and magnetic fields. In a properly terminated transmission line, the magnitude of I_1 will equal that of I_2 with the result that fields at some distance will cancel. In the case of coaxial cable they cancel at the shield, while for balanced line they exist for some distance around the line.

The action of the currents in an ideal line can be modeled as shown in Figure 7-2 in Chapter 7. The model can be analyzed with reasonable accuracy in comparison to real cable if there are at least 10 sections per wavelength, and if the inductors and capacitors are modeled as real elements, including the resistance of the wire and the dielectric loss of the capacitors.

For the case of dc, the wire loss just equals the dc resistance of the wire, a function of its diameter and material. As frequencies increase, *skin effect* results in the current moving to the outer edge of each conductor. This makes the wires electrically appear as tubes, with the tube walls getting thinner as the frequency rises. The thinner walls decrease the effective cross sectional area of the conductors resulting in an increase in resistance and thus increased loss with frequency.

Dielectric Loss

An ideal transmission line would consist of conductors with the insulation between them a perfect lossless vacuum. While some transmission lines approach this, with air (or even special gasses) as the primary dielectric, real lines always have some lossey material between the conductors.

A lossey dielectric has two significant effects on signals: First, it slows the signal to some fraction of the speed of light. This is often an important consideration in multielement driven antennas that rely on accurate phasing of signals, but does not enter into this discussion.

Second, dielectric loss results in yet another contribution to line loss, and this also increases with increasing frequency.

Radiation or Leakage Loss

While generally less significant a loss factor than the previous two, some signal is lost in a real line due to it leaving the transmission line before it reaches the intended load. In a sense this is more a misdirected signal than a lost signal, and, because the signals end up in undesired places, the interference to other systems may be more important than the slight reduction in signal delivered to the desired load. Still, for either reason it can represents a significant issue for real lines.

In the case of coaxial cable, a portion of the shield resistance (depending on the shield coverage) results in a current that appears on the outside of the shield. The outer shield current actually makes the outside of the shield act as an antenna with resulting radiation detectable along the length of the shield. For balanced transmission line, the fields cancel wherever the distance to both wires is the same. For a perfectly installed line, that means all the places on a plane centered between the conductors and perpendicular to the line between them.

If the line is not perfectly installed, there will be some unbalance between the capacitance of each wire to ground resulting in a current unbalance that results in radiation. A similar effect occurs if the load is not perfectly balanced. Even in the case of perfect balance, there is some radiation in directions in which the distance to the wires is different. If the spacing is a small fraction of a wavelength, this radiation is diminished within a few times the wire spacing.

How Can We Determine Loss?

Transmission line loss is a design parameter that is specified by each manufacturer for their cables. The line loss is generally specified over the usual operating range at a number of frequencies, often 1, 10, 100, 1000 and 10,000 MHz.

Matched Loss

Figure 7-3 shows the *matched* loss per 100 feet of representative transmission line types. As you make choices of transmission line, it is important to note that this data is representative — the variation between attenuation of different manufacturers, and even different part numbers from the same manufacturer, can be striking. Check the manufacturer's Web page for the data sheet of the transmission line you are considering to be sure you know what you are getting.

For lengths other than 100 feet, the loss scales linearly. For example if a line has a matched loss of 2 dB at 100 feet, the same line, at the same frequency, will have a loss of 1 dB if 50 feet long, and 5 dB if 250 feet long.

Additional Loss
Due to Mismatch

By now it should come as no surprise to find that a mismatched line has more loss than a matched one. The additional loss due to mismatch is a function of both the mismatch and the loss if matched. Figure 7-4

shows the additional loss in dB that occurs as a result of a line not being matched.

Note that the SWR shown is the SWR as measured, or calculated, at the load not the SWR measured at the transmitter end of the cable. This is particularly important in the case of a lossey line since the loss will reduce both the power reaching the antenna and the power of the reflected wave that is used to determine the SWR. This can give very optimistic, and erroneous results.

To give an example of this effect, consider a 100 W transmitter driving a 100 feet of coax with a loss of 3 dB (50% loss). The antenna will see 50 W of power. Lets say 20% of the power is reflected due to the antenna mismatch. That will result in 10 W being reflected back toward the source. The 3 dB loss results in 5 W showing up as reflected power at the bottom of the cable. This is quite different than if the 100 W were applied to the antenna on lossless line — in that case, a reflected power of 20 W,

not 5 W, would, show up at the SWR measurement device.

Table 9-1 summarizes what we have at the two locations. Note the rather distressing result. A very acceptable measurement of an SWR of 1.6:1 at the bottom of the coax is the result of an unpleasant SWR of 4:1 at the antenna. In this example, our 100 W of power results in only 40 W radiated from the antenna — yet all of our measurements make us think we're doing well. Unfortunately, this example is not unusual, especially at the upper end of HF into the VHF range. If it happens at higher frequencies, it is usually more evident since nothing much ends up going in or out of the system! The sidebar discusses ways that this can be calculated, and perhaps avoided, through the use of software.[1]

[1]J. Hallas, W1ZR, "I Know What's Happening at the Shack — What's Happening at the Other End of my Feed Line?" *QST*, Feb 2007, p 63.

Table 9-1

Forward and Reflected Power and SWR as Seen at Each End of a Transmission Line with 3 dB Loss

Measurement	Bottom of Cable	Top of Cable
Forward Power (W)	100	50
Reflected Power (W)	5	10
Indicated Reflection Coefficient	0.224	0.447
Indicated SWR	1.6	4.0

How is Transmission line Made?

You may wonder what is it about transmission lines that makes their loss performance so different. It all comes down to how and of what they are made. **Figure 9-1** shows typical construction techniques of parallel and coaxial transmission line types. Not shown are lines with mostly air as a dielectric, the lines with the least loss. Parallel line, so-called open-wire line, consists of two parallel bare wires with occasional spacers designed to keep them apart and at about the same distance. The traditional insulators were ceramic, however, recent lines have used plastic or PVC spacers. Mostly air-dielectric

coax is sometimes encountered. Such cable that I've seen is formed from two concentric copper tubes with ceramic donut shaped spacers every foot or so.

The characteristic impedance of cable is a function of conductor diameter and spacing. Thus as line gets larger, each conductor gets larger for the same Z_0 and thus the resistance is reduced, resulting in lower loss with larger cable.

The balanced line (more next chapter) has progressively less attenuation as the Z_0 gets higher (the ratio of series resistance to load resistance goes down) and as the polyethylene

dielectric is replaced by air, partially in the case of window line (C) and more completely in open wire line described above.

Coaxial cable loss is similar in that foam dielectric is part polyethylene and part air. The lines with double (E) and solid metal (F, G) shields have lower resistance and much less leakage.

Perhaps not surprisingly, all the factors that make line have lower attenuation, make it more expensive. Still, in most systems, for reasonable distances, transmission line cost is a small part of total system cost, and often provides a worthwhile investment.

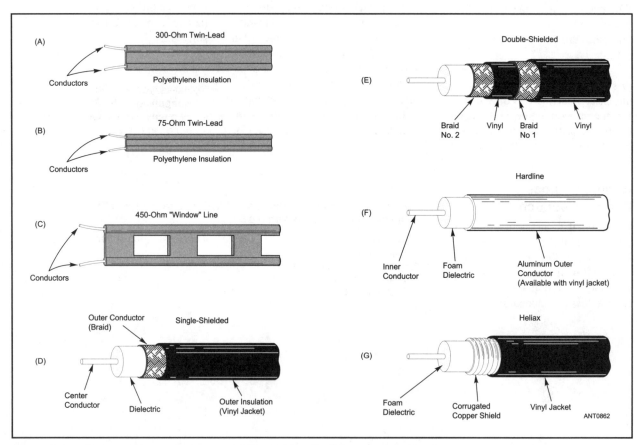

Figure 9-1 — Construction techniques used in making flexible transmission lines.

I Know What's Happening at the Shack — What's Happening at the Other End of my Feed Line?

Joel R. Hallas, W1ZR
Technical Editor, QST

**If you want to find out —
here's the easy way using TLW.**

I'm told that one of the more frequent questions received by *QST's* "Doctor" has to do with folks wanting to determine the impact of transmission line losses on the effectiveness of their antenna system. These questions are often along the lines of "I measure an SWR of 2.5:1 at the transmitter end of 135 feet of RG-8X coaxial cable. My transceiver's auto-tuner can tune it to 1.1, but how can I tell what my losses are?" or "How much difference will I have if I have a tuner at the antenna instead of using the built-in tuner?"

These are important questions that almost every amateur operator is faced with from time to time. An approximate answer can be obtained by using the graphs found in any recent edition of The ARRL Antenna Book showing the loss characteristics of many transmission line types, plus adding in the effect of an SWR greater than 1:1. The SWR at the antenna end can be determined from the bottom end SWR and the cable loss. Using these graphs requires a bit of interpolation or Kentucky windage, but can result in useful data.

But There's an Even Better Way!

Packaged with each of the last few editions of *The ARRL Antenna Book* is a CD containing the pages of the whole Antenna Book as well as some very useful software. The program that I use almost daily is one written by Antenna Book Editor R. Dean Straw, N6BV, called *TLW* for Transmission Line for Windows.

TLW provides a very easy to operate mechanism to determine everything I usually need to know about what's happening on a transmission line. When you open the program, you are presented with a screen as shown in Figure A. This has the values plugged in from the last time you used it, often saving a step. Let's take a quick tour of the inputs:

Cable Type — This allows you to select the cable you would like to analyze. A drop-down box provides for the selection of one of 32 of the most common types of coax and balanced lines. An additional entry is provided for User Defined Transmission Lines that can be specified by propagation velocity and attenuation.

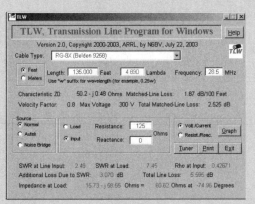

Figure A — The opening screen of *TLW*, illustrating the process described in the article.

Length — In feet or meters, your choice.

Frequency — This is an important parameter when dealing with transmission line effects.

Source — This defines the form of the input impedance data. Generally, you can use NORMAL.

Impedance — The impedance can be specified as what you measure, resistive (real) and reactive (imaginary, minus means capacitive). This could come from your antenna analyzer at either end of the transmission line. Note, if you only know the SWR, not the actual impedance, all is not lost — see below.

Now for the Outputs

SWR — The SWR is provided at each end of the cable. This is an important difference that many people miss, important even with a moderate SWR at the transmitter end, as we'll see — the SWR at the antenna will be much higher due to the cable loss. With TLW, you instantly know the SWR at both ends, and the loss in the cable itself

Rho at Load — This is the reflection coefficient, the fraction of the power reflected back from the load.

Additional Loss Due to SWR — This is one of the answers we were after.

Total Loss — And this is the other, the total loss in the line, including that caused by the mismatch.

But Doctor, What if I can Only Measure the SWR — Not the Actual Impedance?

Often the only measurement data available is the SWR at the transmitter end of the cable. Because the losses are a function of the SWR, not the particular impedance, you can just put in an arbitrary impedance with that same SWR and click the INPUT button. An easy arbitrary impedance to use is just the SWR times the Z_0 of the cable, usually 50 Ω. For example, you could use a resistance of 125 Ω to represent an SWR of 2.5:1. This is what we've done in Figure A, using 135 feet of popular Belden RG-8X.

The results are interesting. Note that the 2.5:1 SWR as seen at the radio on 28.5 MHz results from a 7.45:1 SWR at the antenna — perhaps this is an eye-opener! Note that of the 5.6 dB loss, more than half, or 3.1 dB, is due to the mismatch. Note that if we used something other the actual measured impedance, we can't make use of the impedance data that TLW provides. We can use the SWR and loss data, however, but that's probably what we wanted to find out.

We can now do some "what ifs." We can see how much loss we have on other bands by just changing the frequency. For example, on 80 meters, with the same 2.5:1 at the transmitter end, the SWR at the antenna is about 3:1 and the loss is slightly more than 1 dB. We could also plug in an impedance calculated at the antenna end and see what difference other cable types would make. For example, with the same 28.5 MHz SWR of 7.45 at the antenna and 135 feet of 1/2 inch Andrew Heliax, we will have a total loss of 1.5 dB at 28.5 MHz. Note that the SWR seen at the bottom will now be 5.5:1 and our radio's auto-tuner might not be able to match the new load.

But Wait There's More!

You can also click the GRAPH button and get a plot of either voltage and current or resistance and reactance along the cable. Note that these will only be useful if we have started with actual impedance, rather than SWR.

Pushing the TUNER button results in a page asking you to select some specifications for your tuner parts. TLW effectively designs a tuner of the type you asked for at the shack end of the cable. It also calculates the power lost in the tuner and gives a summary of the transmitted and lost power in watts, so you don't need to calculate it!

When you've finished, be sure to hit the EXIT button, don't just close the window. Otherwise TLW may not start properly the next time you want to use it.

Review Questions

9-1 What parameters make a difference in the matched loss of transmission line, mismatched loss?

9-2 Why is it important to know the SWR at the load, rather than at the transmitter to determine transmission line loss?

9-3 Does coaxial cable or parallel line transmission line tend to have the lowest matched loss?

Chapter 10

Balanced vs Unbalanced Lines

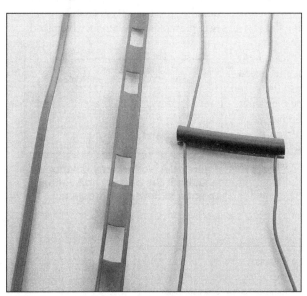

View of three popular types of balanced line. On far left, TV type 300 Ω twinlead, nominal 450 Ω "window" line and 600 Ω open-wire line.

Contents

The careful observer might have noted that in Figure 7-3, in Chapter 7, the lowest loss line was not the fancy, expensive "hardline" coax, but rather the much less expensive balanced open-wire and window line. This is a hard combination to beat — low cost and low attenuation, which explains its popularity. The other side of the coin is that most current radio equipment is designed to operate with unbalanced coaxial line.

What's the Story About Balanced Line?

Before we can go too far, we need to discuss what we mean by balanced and unbalanced. By a balanced system, we mean one in which the two sides are at the same impedance above ground. For example feeding the non ground end of two 100 Ω resistors (see **Figure 10-1**) that have the other end grounded will result in a balanced 200 Ω system. In such a case the voltage on each side will be the same magnitude but 180° out of phase. The magnitude of the currents on each side will also be the same since the voltages and resistances are equal.

Note that the system would be balanced whether or not the ground connection were there. No current flows in the ground lead of the perfectly balanced system, so it could be removed without changing the operational properties. **Figure 10-2** shows two examples of inherently balanced

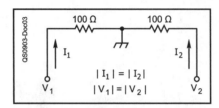

Figure 10-1 — Perfectly balanced load, both the current and voltage on each side will be in balance.

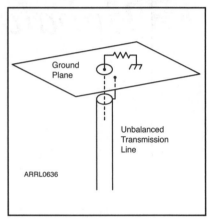

Figure 10-3 — Unbalanced resistive load. The signal is applied with reference to ground.

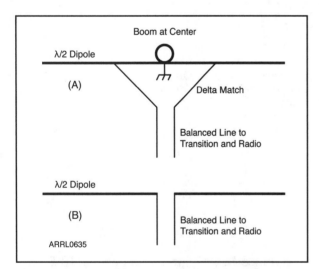

Figure 10-2 — Two examples of inherently balanced antennas, one (delta matched dipole) with a central ground (A) and one (split dipole) without (B).

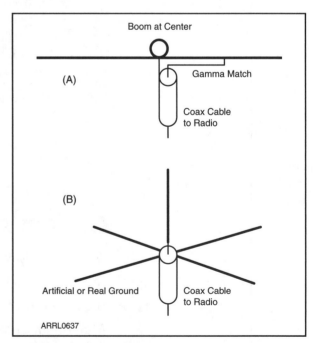

Figure 10-4 — Two examples of inherently unbalanced antennas, a gamma matched dipole at (A) and a vertical monopole at (B).

antennas, one with a central ground (A) and one without (B). The ground in the first is not actually necessary, but can be beneficial for lightning protection purposes. For both cases, we note that some kind of transition is required to shift to an unbalanced system for connection to the radio. The types of transition will be the subject of the next chapter.

An unbalanced system, on the other hand, is fed with respect to ground. That is, one side of the load is at ground potential. **Figure 10-3** is an example of an unbalanced resistive load, and **Figure 10-4** is shows two antennas with inherently unbalanced feed points.

The Benefits of Balanced Line

As noted earlier, balanced line has two primary benefits in comparison to coaxial cable. Most balanced lines, especially those with large portions of air dielectric, such as window line or ladder line, have a significantly lower matched loss than most coaxial cables. Even though their characteristic impedance is often higher than desired for many antenna systems, the total of matched and mismatched loss is generally much less than the loss of coax — particularly if the coax is not well matched to the impedance of the load.

Balanced line is often very conveniently connected to balanced antennas and is most often encountered in that application. It is also

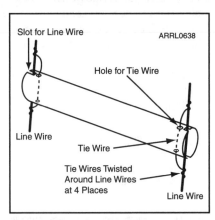

Figure 10-5 — One method of making homemade low loss open wire line. By putting the line in slots and securing with tie wires, sliding the insulators the length of the line can be avoided.

frequently found in very long runs from unbalanced antennas in which the losses (or cost) of coax would be prohibitive. In that case, it may be worth the effort to transition (Chapter 11) from unbalanced to balanced near the antenna and then back at the radio end.

Most balanced line is relatively inexpensive when compared to coax — often an important consideration. Excellent homemade open wire line can be fabricated at low cost from two rolls of wire (stranded works best, in my experience, particularly if subject to flexing) and insulators made from inexpensive household PVC tubing. **Figure 10-5** shows one technique.

The Downsides of Balanced Line

As with most aspects of life, there are downsides of balanced line as well as benefits. While coax cable, with its fields contained within the shield, can be rolled, buried (if it has a direct burial rating) or installed within or near pipes without impacting performance, this is not true of balanced line. With balanced line, the fields conveying the signal down the line are significant not only between the wires but outside as well for a distance of a few times the wire spacing. This means that balanced line can't be placed on the ground, run in metal ducts, run through lossey material or rolled up, without causing additional loss.

While fields at a distance from balanced line are small, nearby fields can cause interference to other systems, particularly those interconnected by wiring. In addition, on receive, balanced line can pick up interfering signals from computers and other systems if run too close to them.

Another potential issue, particularly with the twinlead or window line variants of balanced line is a change in characteristics when wet. Rainwater can accumulate on the web material between the conductors resulting in a change to the dielectric properties of the line.[1]

There are a few things that can be done if this is a problem:

• Some have been known to care-

[1] B. Allison, WB1GCM, J. Hallas, W1ZR," A Closer Look at Window Transmission Line," *QST*, Nov 2009, pp 66-67.

fully cut away some of the web to reduce the water collection surface. To avoid weakening the line, don't cut into the wire if you try this.

• In the "old days," some amateurs waxed their twinlead. This was reputed to cause the water to bead up and run off. Remaining water would be concentrated in droplets leaving most of the dielectric clear. I haven't seen any data on how effective this actually is, nor have I heard of any modern amateurs having the patience to actually do it!

In many cases, these potential problems can be largely avoided through careful planning and installation design. If not, it is sometimes efficient to make a transition to coax cable for some portion of the transmission line run.

What About Unbalanced Currents on Coax?

In the above section, it probably sounded as if the fields in coax are completely within the coax, thus avoiding the downsides of parallel or balanced line. That is true for the ideal case of properly terminated coax, however, there are at least three ways in which coax can suffer the same limitations as balanced line in this regard. In all cases, this results in currents on the outside of the shield. I have listed them in order of likelihood and severity, based on my experience.

• The coax is not terminated in a properly unbalanced load. This happens if the coax shield is not connected to a ground reference at the antenna. The result is that the current to the shield splits between the inside and outside of the shield.

• The coax run is coupled to the antenna such that the net coupling is not balanced at the cable. For a center fed antenna, coax should be run perpendicular to the antenna element so the coupling from each side cancels. If not, even with proper termination, there will be currents induced on the outside of the shield. For some antennas, monopoles or off center fed antennas for example, it is almost impossible to avoid such coupling.

• The coax shield itself can be leaky. The shield of most coax is not perfect and some is far from it. The specification sheets often list "percent coverage" indicating how well the shield covers the center conductor. Cables with lower numbers will be leakier than those with higher coverage. The current tends to increase as it is coupled over longer distances.

In many cases, the effects of such currents are small, but be aware that they exist and check them out if strange problems appear. A quick test is to note the antenna tuning or SWR as you run your hand along the cable. With properly installed and isolated coax, the tuning shouldn't change.

What Happens If I Feed my Dipole Directly with Coax?

Many amateurs connect their coax directly to a balanced center fed dipole — center conductor to one side, shield to the other as shown in **Figure 10-6**. This is a topic of some controversy with as many folk swearing that it works fine, as there are those who say it causes problems.

The reason for the disagreement may be that there are actually people who end up in both camps because of the dimensions of their system. Recall that due to skin effect, the currents on the inside of the shield of a coax cable are within a small thickness from the inside wall. Thus the outside of the coax acts like a completely different conductor — it's as if the insulated coax were installed in a pipe that is connected to the shield at the antenna end.

If the half wave dipole in Figure 10-6 had a center impedance of 50 Ω, typical for relatively low dipoles, the balanced antenna would act like a 25 Ω load to each connection of the coax, Z_{ANT} in Figure 10-6. The impedance of the outside of the shield at the antenna is a bit less obvious. This impedance depends on the impedance to ground at the bottom of the cable, usually at a ground level and grounded entrance panel, and the length of the cable between the antenna and the ground terminal.

Just as with an antenna wire or transmission line, this impedance varies depending on electrical length. If the ground impedance is low and the length is a multiple of a half wave, the impedance at the top will repeat and also be low. On the other hand, if

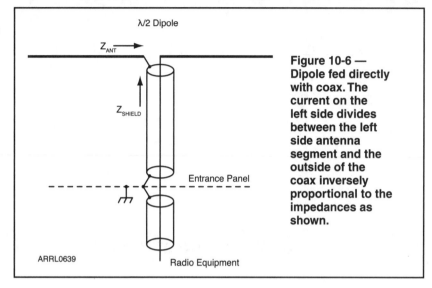

Figure 10-6 — Dipole fed directly with coax. The current on the left side divides between the left side antenna segment and the outside of the coax inversely proportional to the impedances as shown.

the length is an odd number of quarter wavelengths, the impedance will reverse and be high. Lengths in between will result in intermediate values of impedance, both resistive and reactive.

If the impedance at the top of the shield is of the same order as the half dipole impedance, the current will divide between the two paths. This can have three effects:

• If the ground at the bottom is not of a very low impedance, RF currents can enter the radio room and cause a number of strange equipment problems such as feedback or transmitter lockup.

• The radiation from the transmission line will distort the antenna pattern, usually adding an omnidirectional vertical component. For a single element antenna, this may not be all bad, since it may tend to fill in the nulls that otherwise would be in some

directions. For a directional array, however, such radiation will reduce both forward gain and front-to-back ratio — not good things.

• If the transmission line runs past sensitive electronic systems, fire or intrusion alarm wiring, computers or telephone systems, for example, the radiation may cause harmful interference in either direction.

Note that for a low impedance antenna, such as our dipole and most coax fed antennas, there are a small number of lengths that will result in such problems. With a multiband antenna the possibilities of problems increase directly with the number of bands covered. Thus it is not surprising that many don't think any precautions are necessary. Still, it can't hurt to avoid them, much of the subject of the next chapter.

Review Questions

10-1 Under what conditions is unbalanced transmission line most appropriate for antenna to radio connections?

10-2 Repeat question 10-1 for balanced transmission line.

10-3 Why do some people report problems with balanced antennas connected directly to coax while others observe no difficulties?

Chapter 11

So What's a Balun, an Unun, a Choke?

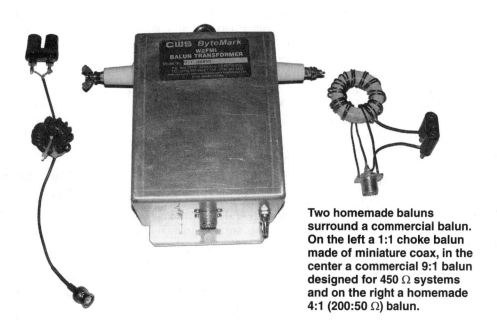

Two homemade baluns surround a commercial balun. On the left a 1:1 choke balun made of miniature coax, in the center a commercial 9:1 balun designed for 450 Ω systems and on the right a homemade 4:1 (200:50 Ω) balun.

Contents

Baluns are devices that provide a transition between unbalanced and balanced systems, impedance transformation or a combination of both. The name *balun* comes from *BAL*-anced to *UN*balanced and each part is pronounced the same way as in the separate words.

Sometimes you will encounter an *unun*. The unun (*UN*balanced to *UN*balanced) provides an interconnection between two unbalanced systems, either to change the system impedance, to force all currents into the inside of a coaxial transmission line or usually both.

A *choke* refers to an inductance that offers a high impedance over a particular frequency range. A choke wound with coaxial cable has its high impedance only to currents on the outside of the coax shield, the inductances of the inner conductors effectively cancel. As we will discuss, such a choke can be used either as a balun or an unun.

When are Baluns Necessary?

We have discussed unbalanced line such as coax cable, balanced line such as twinlead, window or ladder line as well as balanced and unbalanced loads. We should point out that virtually all transmitters or transceivers built since the 1950s are designed to work into an unbalanced load — made evident by the coaxial connector used for the antenna connection.[1]

There are many antennas designed to operate with a coaxial cable connection. These antennas can be connected directly to the radio with coaxial cable if they present the desired load to the transmitter. In this case, no transition is required, the entire system is unbalanced. This system can work well and neither an antenna tuner, nor a balun, is required for proper operation. The one exception occurs if there is coupling from the antenna to the transmission line, resulting in undesired coax shield current in which case a common mode choke is recommended.

What's Wrong with this Picture?

The unbalanced antenna, unbalanced transmission line and unbalanced radio make a simple and straightforward arrangement that is easy to operate. Unfortunately, in many cases, the antenna only provides an appropriate match over a narrow frequency range — often narrower than an amateur band, for example. This has two effects:

• If the SWR at the transmitter reaches a higher value than the transmitter can operate into, it will usually reduce the power output to avoid damage to internal components.

• While the losses for matched coaxial cable can be made acceptable by selecting the proper cable for the frequency and length, the losses generally go up quickly with increasing SWR. As noted previously, this actually makes the SWR at the transmitter look better; however, significant power may be lost (turned into heat) in the cable.

Many amateurs choose instead to use a balanced antenna fed with lower loss balanced line in this case. As will be discussed later, this often makes what would be a single band antenna, if fed with coax, into a multiband antenna. We then are faced with a balanced load and an unbalanced transmitter output connector.

What Happens if We Plug the Balanced Line into our Coax Connector?

While not recommended. you can actually make the connection, if pressed. Arguably, it is not much worse than the previously discussed case of hooking unbalanced coax line to a dipole antenna. In this case, however, the shield side of the transmitter output is connected to ground and a fraction of your output power will flow in that direction radiating within the room instead of towards the desired direction. If the ground is not solid, you can end up with RF on all your equipment, causing various strange and sometimes uncomfortable effects.

[1]The shift to the use of coaxial cable happened because coaxial cable became available after WW2 coincidentally with the popularity of broadcast television. Transmitters with shielding, filtering and coaxial RF connections were less likely, if properly designed, to cause interference problems with TV sets.

What do We Mean by Balanced to Unbalanced?

The balun makes the transition from an unbalanced system, such as the transceiver, to a balanced system, such as a balanced transmission line. A balun can be used between a balanced dipole and a coaxial cable to avoid the problem of current being driven down the shield of the coax, or it can be used between the unbalanced transmitter and a balanced line to result in the current going towards the antenna as shown in **Figure 11-1**.

As noted previously, sometimes a balun is also used to transform impedances. For example, in the case of a 50 Ω antenna, a 50 Ω transmitter and the use of low loss 450 Ω transmission line, a balun with a 9:1 impedance transformation ratio allows a straightforward interconnection as shown in **Figures 11-2** and **11-3**.

Of course there is still no such thing as a free lunch. In order to use the low loss balanced line in this configuration, the added loss in each of the two baluns must be considered as part of the equation. Measurements I've taken of commercial HF 9:1 baluns have indicated that losses of about 0.5 dB each should be anticipated. It doesn't usually take too long a run of line before the balun loss is compensated for by the higher loss of the coax. This depends on both length and frequency.

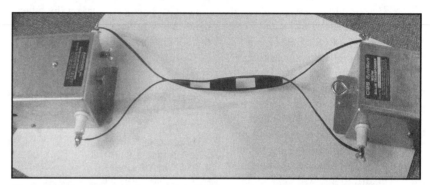

Figure 11-3 — Photo of a model of the system of Figure 11-2 using commercial 9:1 baluns. The twist in the window line is intentional. An occasional twist reduces wind effects and tends to maintain balance in the system if near objects.

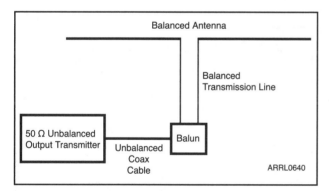

Figure 11-1 — A balun inserted between the unbalanced output of a transmitter or transceiver and a balanced antenna system.

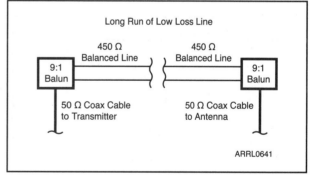

Figure 11-2 — The use of baluns with a 9:1 impedance transformation ratio makes it easy to use low loss 450 Ω balanced transmission line for long runs.

Balun Location

A balun can be inserted anywhere in a system between a coaxial connection and the balanced load. As shown in **Figures 11-4** and **11-5**, the connection between an unbalanced radio and a balanced dipole can include a balun at either end of the transmission line run. Here we have used a dipole with a *delta match* adjusted to provide a 450 Ω balanced load at the antenna.

While the configurations of Figures 11-4 and 11-5 appear to be equivalent, and both can work well as shown, there are advantages to each:

• The configuration of Figure 11-4, using a long run of 450 Ω balanced line, will usually have less loss than the system in Figure 11-5 due to the characteristics of the transmission line. The difference will depend on the frequency, line length and type of coax. Some representative loss figures are shown in **Table 11-1**.

• Using coaxial cable for the run, as in Figure 11-5, has its own advantages. The principal one is that coax is less fussy about how it is placed than is balanced line. While coax can be run in metal conduit, coiled up and some types can be buried — this is not the case with balanced line. With properly installed coax, the fields are entirely within the coax, making it insensitive to its surroundings. Parallel conductor balanced line, on the other hand, has significant fields between the conductors and extending out to a few times the wire separation in all directions. In order to obtain the benefits of such line, it needs to be spaced that far from metal structures and lossey media.

Note also that it is not necessary to have the run entirely with one type of line. For example, a long aerial run of balanced line can be transitioned to coax near the radio with a short run of coax going through conduit or other balanced line hostile environments.

Table 11-1

Comparison of Transmission Line Losses of Different Lines at Different Frequencies

Line Type	Matched Loss at Frequency (MHz, dB per 100 feet)			
	1	10	100	1000*
Balanced Line				
300 Ω Transmit Twinlead	0.09	0.3	1.1	3.9
450 Ω Window Line	0.02	0.08	0.3	1.1
600 Ω Open Wire Line	0.02	0.06	0.2	0.75
Coax Cable	1	10	100	1000
RG-58	0.37	1.4	5.3	20
RG-213	0.18	0.7	2.5	8.6
LMR-400	0.12	0.39	1.3	4.2

*Spacing may be too wide for efficient operation at this frequency.

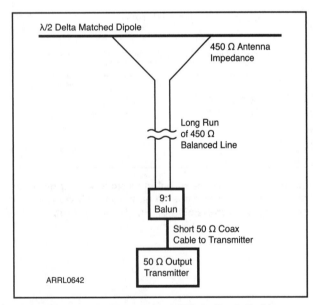

Figure 11-4 — Delta matched 450 Ω dipole fed by low loss 450 Ω balanced line to a 9:1 balun at the transmitter.

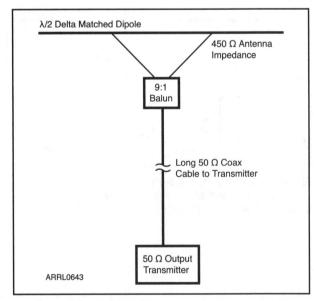

Figure 11-5 — Dipole fed by a 9:1 balun and 50 Ω coaxial cable to the transmitter.

The Different Balun Configurations

There are a number of different balun configurations. They range from simple chokes that force (most of) the current that otherwise would be on the shield of coax to the intended load to more complex devices that combine balanced to unbalanced transitions and impedance transformations in a single device. The following is a summary of the more common types.

Choke Baluns

Choke baluns are found on the coax side of a balanced to unbalanced transition. As noted previously, if a balanced load, such as a dipole antenna, is fed directly by coax, the current on the shield side of the connection will split between the connected half dipole and the outside of the shield in a ratio inversely proportional to the two impedances. The idea of the choke balun is to increase the impedance of the outside of the shield by adding inductance and thus reducing the current that flows down the outside of the shield. If no current were to flow down the shield the current to the each side of the antenna would be the same as if the coax were a balanced line on the antenna side.

Air wound coax loops — The simplest form of choke is just a coil of coaxial cable as shown in **Figure 11-6**. Note that for the so called *differential mode* signal, the desired signal inside the coax, this coil just acts like a few feet of transmission line. The *common mode* signal, any

[2]R. D. Straw, Editor, *The ARRL Antenna Book,* 21st Edition. Available from your ARRL dealer or the ARRL Bookstore, ARRL order no. 9876. Telephone 860-594-0355, or toll-free in the US 888-277-5289; **www.arrl.org/arrl-store**; **pubsales@arrl.org**.

undesired signal on the outside of the coax, sees the effect of the coil inductance.

This configuration has been evaluated at length with results reported in *The ARRL Antenna Book*.[2] An example is a six turns in single layer coil of coax with a diameter of 4.25 inches. This coil will have an impedance ranging from 514 Ω at 14 MHz to 1079 Ω at 29 MHz, very suitable for feeding a dipole or triband Yagi, for example. Such coils are sometimes scramble wound rather than being wound in a single layer. While

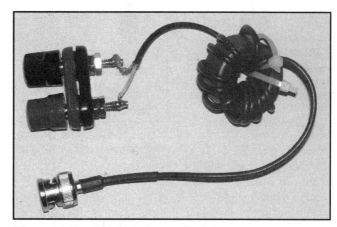

Figure 11-7 — Choke balun made by passing multiple turns of coax through a ferrite toroidal core.

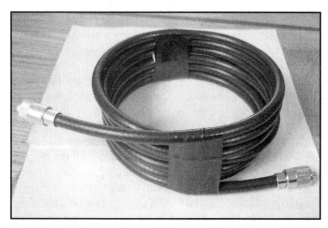

Figure 11-6 — Choke balun made from a coil of coax. Such a balun can be effective over about a 2:1 frequency range.

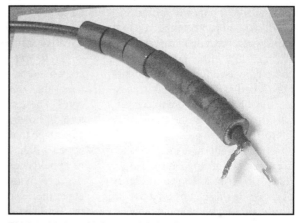

Figure 11-8 — Using multiple single turn "coils" in series — a good solution for large diameter or stiff coax.

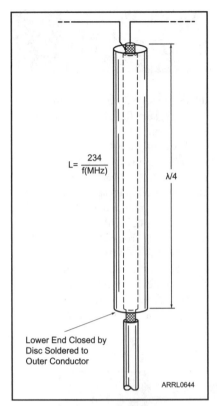

$$L = \frac{234}{f(MHz)}$$

λ/4

Lower End Closed by
Disc Soldered to
Outer Conductor

ARRL0644

Figure 11-9 — The bazooka quarter wave choke balun made by providing a shorted line section around the shield of a coax cable.

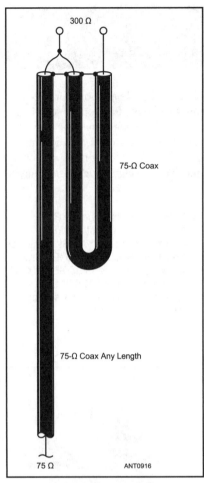

300 Ω

75-Ω Coax

75-Ω Coax Any Length

75 Ω   ANT0916

Figure 11-10 — The ½ wave 4:1 impedance transforming balun.

they can be moderately effective, they usually suffer at higher frequencies due to excessive capacitance between turns. The only other effect of the coax coil is any attenuation due to the additional length of coax, in this case about 7 feet.

Ferrite toroid coils — The effectiveness of a choke coil can be improved by winding it on a ferrite toroidal core, as shown in **Figure 11-7**. The coil can be either a pair of wires wound together around the core or coax cable, either extra thin coax, or the type used for the transmission line. A coil of 12 turns of thin coax on a type FT240-61 core makes an effective choke over the range from 1.8 to 30 MHz.

A popular alternate method is to use a number of single turn ferrite "coils" in series as shown in **Figure 11-8**. While this can be effective, it is worth pointing out that the inductance of N such inductors in series equals N times the inductance of a single

inductor. On the other hand, the inductance of multiple turns through a single toroid goes up by the square of the number of turns. Still if the coax is thick, or hard to bend tightly, this is a very workable solution. It has the additional advantage that the capacitance between "turns" is less than with a coil, so it will tend to be more effective at higher frequencies.

Ferrite rod coils — Some baluns are wound on sections of ferrite rod rather than the toroid, donut shaped, cores. These can work as well as the toroids, however, the toroids have the advantage that the fields are contained within the core, while the rods have fields between the ends outside the core, making them more fussy about their surroundings. Sometimes the available space will point towards one versus the other. All other things being equal, I prefer the self shielding

toroids, if feasible.

Transmission line sections — A quarter wave long section of transmission line, shorted at the far end, has a high impedance at the near end. This property can be used as a choke at the particular frequency that the line section is that length (or odd multiples). This is called a bazooka, due to the use of large concentric structures as shown in **Figure 11-9**. This is a particularly popular arrangement at VHF and higher, since the dimensions are reasonable and wideband properties of the ferrite baluns and chokes are often not required.

Transformer Baluns

The half-wave coax loop — One of the early forms of transforming balun was also made of coax cable, this time an electrical ½ wave long. This cable was formed into a loop with one end on each side of the balanced load as shown in **Figure 11-10**. The unbalanced line was connected to one side of the balanced load.

The half wave loop provides a copy of the signal from the coax feedline delayed by 180°, and thus out of phase. Each of the two signals see an impedance of half of total 300 Ω load, or 150 Ω. Because the impedance on a halfwave (or multiple) of a transmission line repeats itself, the loop will bring the 150 Ω impedance back to the feedline junction. The parallel combination of the two 150 Ω signals at the feedline junction is thus ¼ of the total load or 75 Ω. Note that since a half wave length of transmission line repeats whatever impedance is there, this will transform any impedance to ¼ the value on the single frequency.

The half-wave loop transforming balun is very efficient, with the only loss or imbalance a result of the loss in the loop of coax. A disadvantage is that they only operate on (or close to) the frequency at which the loop is ½ wave (or multiples) long. These are frequently used to feed VHF and UHF Yagis that operate on a narrow band of frequencies making the narrow bandwidth irrelevant.

Ferrite transformers — Broadband

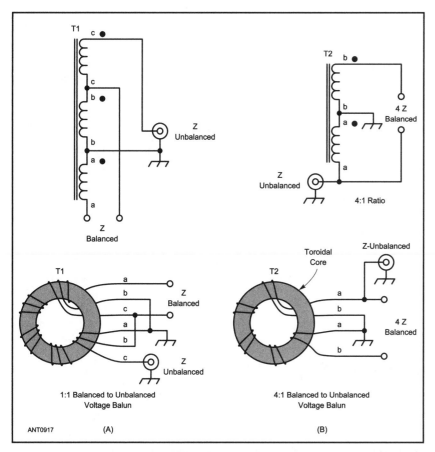

Figure 11-11 — Schematic and pictorial view of a broadband ferrite core 4:1 impedance transforming balun.

baluns can be made using the same kind of ferrite structures described previously as transformers. They frequently are made with multiple windings that can be connected in series or parallel to provide multiple transformation ratios. The 4:1 balun shown in **Figure 11-11** is an example of such a balun that functions similarly to the ½ wave coax loop balun.

Current and Voltage Baluns — Depending on the details of their design, a balun can be made to force either the current *or* the voltage on the balanced side to equal each other. Note that in a perfectly balanced load, in which each side has the same impedance to ground, if the voltages are equal so will be the currents and vice versa.

Unfortunately, in our real world, often an intended balanced load, isn't quite. For example, an otherwise balanced antenna may become unbalanced if one side is closer to the ground, or to a metal structure, than the other. If the balun is intended, as most are, to keep currents off the outside of coax shields, then by forcing the currents to be equal your objective is most likely to be met.

Selecting Baluns for Use in Your System

Within the constraints listed above, any of the general type of baluns described can be selected for use. Most baluns have a specified input and output impedance and power rating. These should be matched to your application. The transformation ratio does not apply for any impedance, rather for the design center of the balun. For example a 4:1 balun designed to transform a 200 Ω balanced load to 50 Ω coax, can not counted on to provide a 4:1 transformation to a 2000 Ω balanced load.

In practice, the transformation is likely to be close to the specified ratio for perhaps a 4:1 mismatch — in the previous case that would be from 50 to 800 Ω. Outside of that range, they may continue to function as a balun, however, the transformation ratio will be different and the losses will tend to increase.

A mismatch will also increase the stress on the balun. The current or the voltage will be higher by the square root of the SWR or mismatch ratio and thus the ratings should be increased appropriately. After use (with power off) a good check at a 100 W or higher power station is to put a finger on the balun to check the temperature. Any increase above ambient is cause for reconsideration.

Review Questions

11-1 Provide three reasons for using a balun.

11-2 What are the relative advantages of having a balun at a balanced
      antenna feed point versus having a long run of balanced line to a
      balun near the transmitter?

11-3 What are the consequences of operating a balun at an impedance far
      from its design point?

Chapter 12

Balanced Antenna Tuners

A classic 275 W E. F. Johnson "Matchbox" balanced antenna tuner from the 1950s. Still a viable tuner useful to 750 W PEP and available at hamfests and auction sites. A 1 kW model, useful above the US legal limit, was also offered.

Contents

We've been talking about antenna tuners and balanced line in the same sentence, even though we haven't addressed the issue of the kind of tuners to use with a balanced load. Now it's time.

What's a Balanced Tuner?

While we haven't specifically addressed the question, the tuners we've been talking about so far have been really what could be called *unbalanced* tuners. You can usually spot an unbalanced tuner by its input and output connector arrangements. In some cases, they have a coax connector for unbalanced cable on both the radio and antenna system sides. Other unbalanced tuners have a coax connector for the radio side and a single terminal intended for a wire antenna and another for a ground connection.

Some unbalanced tuners have another pair of connectors that are designated for "balanced loads" but the transition occurs after the tuner function using an internal balun. While these can be useful for driving balanced loads, as we will discuss, they are really two distinct pieces, an unbalanced tuner followed by a balun.

Enter a Truly Balanced Tuner

The tuner configurations shown in Figure 3-3, in Chapter 3, are all inherently unbalanced since ground is on one side of each. Any of them can be converted to a balanced configuration by essentially providing a mirror image on the other side of ground. The configurations of Figure 3-3 are shown in balanced form in **Figure 12-1**. A quick look at the figure will indicate that we now have something we probably didn't want — a balanced to balanced tuner!

The one configuration that can be easily transformed to a balanced to unbalanced tuner is the tuned transformer in Figure 12-1 (A). This is because the transformer coupling to the radio (left) side of the transformer does not maintain the same ground reference. Thus one side of the primary (left) winding can be grounded

resulting in an unbalanced connection. This is exactly what the 1950s era Johnson Matchbox did, perhaps explaining why it is still in demand today.

Unbalancing One Side

The other configurations in Figure 12-1 require a balun on the 50 Ω side to fit into coaxial fed systems. While this may seem about the same as putting the balun on the antenna side of the tuner (more in next section), the difference here is that we transform the widely variable balanced antenna system impedance on the right side to a 50 Ω balanced load on the left in Figure 12-1. We then can use a 1:1 50 Ω balun to transform to unbalanced for coax connectivity. Alternately, some tuners are designed to transform to a 200 Ω balanced

load, to be followed by a 4:1 balun for connectivity to 50 Ω coax.

In either the 1:1 or 4:1 case, we have the advantage that the baluns are operating at their design impedance. They will offer minimum loss and will operate with their expected transformation ratios.

There's Always a Price

A possible downside of the balanced antenna tuner designs is that the nature of the beast requires significantly more — but not quite twice — as many components as the same unbalanced configuration. The usual antenna tuner components, for medium to high power tuners, are both large and pricy. This results in ramifications in terms of both cost and size. There is, after all, still no such thing as a free lunch.

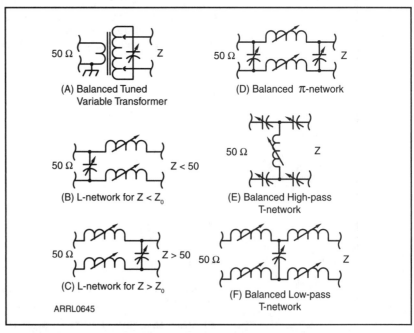

(A) Balanced Tuned
Variable Transformer

(B) L-network for Z < Z₀

(C) L-network for Z > Z₀

(D) Balanced π-network

(E) Balanced High-pass
T-network

(F) Balanced Low-pass
T-network

ARRL0645

Figure 12-1 — Configurations of balanced antenna tuner versions of the unbalanced tuners in Figure 3-3, in Chapter 3.

A Balanced Tuner versus an Unbalanced Tuner with a Balun

As you look over the features of commercial antenna tuners, you will see many with "balanced outputs." In most cases, these are inherently unbalanced tuners, with a balun on the antenna side to transform to a balanced load. Many people, including your humble servant, have been happily using such tuners for years — so what's the problem?

Well, the simple answer is — there may not be a problem! If the impedance at the bottom of your balanced feed line (generally quite different from either the antenna impedance or the transmission line characteristic impedance, if the line is not matched to the antenna) can transform to an unbalanced impedance through the balun without difficulty — there is no problem — you're done!

On the other hand, if the impedance at the balun is very different from its design point, you may have a number of problems, most significantly loss in the balun. While balun loss is not great in its own right — to-roid cores are not very good heat radiators. Any balun loss will transform itself into heat and may destroy the balun's ferrite core in the process.

The Good News Is

While there are exceptions, many unbalanced tuners, including those with a balun for balanced loads, offer additional features compared to many "balanced" tuners. My fairly typical unbalanced L-network tuner, for example, has three outputs for unbalanced coax terminations and a fourth that can either be coax or balanced, using an internal 4:1 balun on the output side. In addition to my main balanced multiband antenna, I have a few other antennas that are fed by coax. Thus the tuner provides a convenient point for them all to come together with easy switching between them. With a single switch on the tuner, I can instantly select any of the four antennas — either through the tuner, or bypassing the tuner, if they are matched systems. Most balanced tuners just provide a connection to a single balanced antenna system.

In terms of keeping common mode RF currents out of your station, it really doesn't matter which side of the tuner has the balun — its choking impedance has the same effect.

If it Doesn't Play

If an unbalanced tuner with a balun doesn't work well with your antenna system on a particular band, you may be able to recover. The fact that it doesn't tune usually means that the balanced line has a high SWR (if it were matched, to say 450 Ω, the tuner and balun combination could probably handle it without difficulty). Because of the nature of the mismatched line, changing the length will have a profound effect on the impedance as seen by the tuner. Try inserting about ⅛ wavelength of line and see what happens. Be sure to observe the usual cautions about balanced line — such as not coiling it up.

Another Possibility — The "Hot" Tuner

Impedance transformation through an unbalanced tuner will not "know" it is unbalanced unless one side of the tuner is grounded. Thus it is quite possible to use an inherently unbalanced tuner into a balanced load if it is isolated from ground. This can be accomplished as shown in **Figure 12-2** for a remote automatic tuner.

The configuration in **Figure 12-3** makes this quite convenient, however, it can also be accomplished using a manual tuner in the station. The difficulty with the tuner in the station is that it generally is designed so that the cabinet is at what it thinks is "ground" potential. If it is isolated from ground, the whole cabinet is at the potential of half the RF voltage feeding the antenna. This can be uncomfortable for the operator, unless she uses oven mitts to make adjustments. An unsuspecting cat can get quite a curl as it passes by during a transmission!

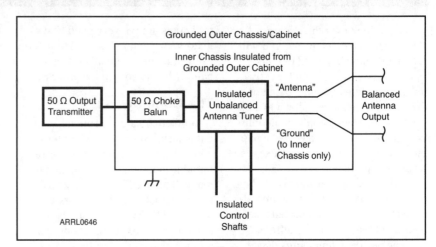

Figure 12-3 — Manually tuned version of an unbalanced tuner isolated from ground driving a balanced load. Note the insulated additional layer of cabinetry.

The hot chassis problem has been solved by at least one published design in which what would be the cabinet is insulated from and inside an additional cabinet with insulated shaft extensions on the controls as shown in **Figure 12-3**. I'm not aware that this has been offered as a commercial product, however, it is feasible — if not simple to implement.

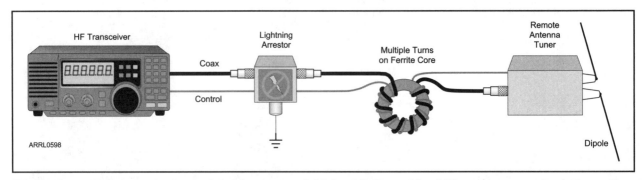

Figure 12-2 — Unbalanced tuner isolated from ground driving a balanced load. The common mode choke on the radio side maintains the balance on the antenna side. Note that it is necessary to provide a choke on all balun connections, as shown, in order to elevate the whole tuner above RF ground.

Review Questions

12-1 Why might an inherently balanced tuner be a good idea?

12-2 What difference does it make whether a balun is on the input or output of an antenna tuner?

12-3 What kind of problems might you have using an unbalanced tuner with a balanced load?

Chapter 13

Antennas That Work Well with Antenna Tuners

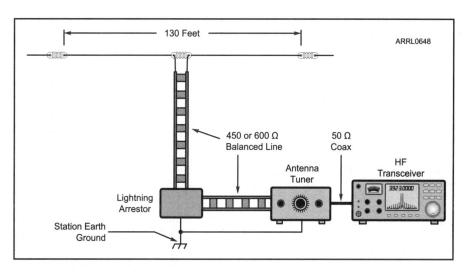

The center-fed Zepp is a very popular antenna with those having a wide-range antenna tuner.

Contents

There's no magic antenna that goes well with a tuner — in fact, virtually any antenna can benefit from a tuner under some circumstances. Here we will discuss how a tuner can increase the flexibility and usefulness of some popular antennas.

The Coax Fed Dipole

In Chapter 2, we discussed the nominally matched dipole and the limitations on its bandwidth within a given SWR. For example, to have a single low 80 meter dipole be useful across the entire band, we may need to deal with an SWR as high as a 10:1 as shown in Figure 2-7, in Chapter 2, although at many heights, the SWR will not rise beyond 5 or 6:1 at band edges. Most other examples shown in Chapter 2 have more reasonable SWR characteristics. Still, in many cases an SWR higher than 2:1 may be encountered, requiring an antenna tuner to permit proper transmitter operation at band edges.

A Dipole Operated on an Odd Harmonic

A special case of the dipole is one used on its third harmonic. A very popular amateur antenna is a 40 meter (7 to 7.3 MHz in the US) dipole also operated on 15 meters (21 to 21.450 MHz). This is often stated as if it were a straightforward arrangement, however, it is just a bit more difficult to achieve than would be implied by some. A tuner makes it much easier. The difficulties arise particularly due to two factors:

• The nominal impedance of a ¾ λ dipole in free space is about 110 Ω, rather than 72 Ω for a λ/2 dipole. While the actual impedance will vary above and below this number, depending on height above ground, this often gives us a higher SWR than 2:1 to start with.

• The third harmonic of 7.15 MHz, the center of the 40 meter band, is 21.45 MHz, the very top of the 15 meter band.

Figure 13-1 shows the modeled SWR of a wire 40 meter dipole cut for mid band at a height of 40 feet. Figure 13-2 shows the SWR of the same antenna operated on 15 meters. Obviously, this isn't going to work out

as well as some folks hypothesize.

Many wide range tuners could compensate for the SWR at the transmitter. As discussed in Chapter 7, however, the losses in a coax cable with a 10:1 SWR at 21 MHz may result in more loss than can generally be tolerated, although it certainly could be used in a pinch. Because the losses in mismatched coax are less at lower frequencies, the concept can be salvaged by optimizing the dipole as a 15 meter ¾ λ dipole with the results shown in **Figures 13-3** and **13-4**.

Note that the lengthened antenna has an SWR of less than 3:1 across all of 15 meters, significantly reducing the transmission line loss associated with Figure 13-2. While the SWR on 40 meters is no longer delightful, it is reasonable from a transmission line loss standpoint. The resulting antenna can work well with some nominal "3:1" SWR tuners that work beyond

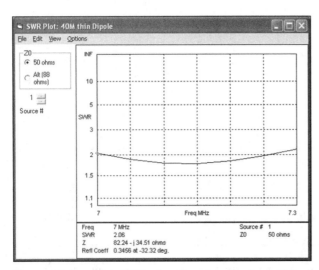

Figure 13-1 — 50 Ω SWR of a 40 meter dipole at 40 feet cut for mid band.

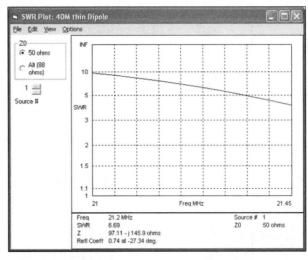

Figure 13-2 — SWR of the 40 meter dipole of Figure 13-1 across 15 meters.

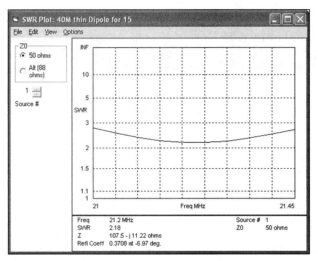

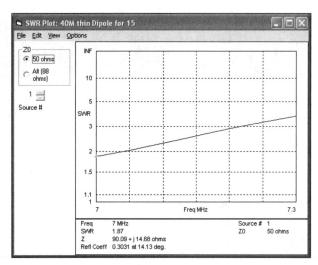

Figure 13-3 — SWR of the 40 meter dipole of Figure 13-1 lengthened to be optimized for 15 meters across 15 the 15 meter band.

Figure 13-4 — SWR of the lengthened (15 meter optimized) 40 meter dipole of Figure 13-3 across 40 meters.

their specs, and is an easy job for wider range tuners.

Dipoles Can Benefit

The preceding examples illustrate ways in which a simple dipole can benefit from an antenna tuner. For any dipole, the tuner can compensate for imperfect length adjustment, often a convenience. The one caution is that even if the tuner can match the resulting impedance, the loss in the mismatched transmission line between the tuner and the antenna can be an issue, even if all seems well at the transmitter. Take another look at Chapter 7.

Tuned Yagi Arrays

We often think of the popular HF Yagi beam antenna as one that is fed directly with 50 Ω coax with low SWR and without any need for a tuner. This is certainly the sense one gets from the specification sheet, yet some highly tuned Yagis, particularly those operating on multiple bands, have trouble providing a close match from band edge to band edge, particularly if optimized for the CW or SSB segment. In most cases, even though the SWR may be marginal at the far edge, there is still beneficial gain and front to back ratio. This is exactly the place for a limited range internal tuner to be applied, since the SWR is often less than 3:1. My sense is this is what they had in mind when these 3:1 tuners were designed — compensating for the just out of tune coax fed dipole or Yagi.

Single Wire Fed Antennas

There are a number of antennas that are designed to be fed as a single wire, without any transmission line. Some are field expedients, however, others are well thought out designs that can offer excellent performance.

Single Wire Antennas

Single wire antennas go back to the very beginning of amateur radio — the days before anyone thought of a transmission line. The most commonly used transmitting antenna in the early days was a short vertical (we're talking below 200 meters, so everything was short!) with top capacitance loading of multiple horizontal wires. They were used on shipboard, shore and ham stations alike, and worked well enough to get the signals through.

These days, a "random length" single wire is often used as an easy to deploy temporary antenna or, for some, using very thin wire, as an unnoticeable stealthy antenna if neighbors or deed restrictions object to "antennas." They can be effective, especially if fed against a good ground system, and if they are at least $\lambda/4$ long at the lowest frequency. Such a $\lambda/4$ wire fed against ground even has a name! This is called a Marconi antenna, and yes. it dates back more than a century.

Random wire antennas will still work if shorter, but ground losses rapidly reduce efficiency as lengths get much shorter than $\lambda/4$.

The success of such single wiere antennas depends on all the usual factors including height, length, and ground conditions all played against desired frequency and geographical coverage. With a ground mounted radio and a higher wire antenna, there will always be some vertically and often horizontally polarized radiation as well. The combination can provide a useful mix of coverage, although the coverage in any direction will not be as good as that of an antenna designed for the job.

The key element in making such an antenna play is a wide range antenna tuner that can match the widely variable load of the single wire on multiple bands to the 50 Ω that modern radios require. So we have a place here for the antenna tuner, the question is "which place."

Antenna Tuner at the Shack — This can work and has been done, but in the most successful implementations, the antenna tuner is near the boundary between indoors and out. In some stations, that boundary is within or at the edge of the shack eliminating the distinction.

A portion of a radiating antenna inside a building is generally asking for some kind of trouble. First there is the RF safety issue as applied to any people inside the structure. Even if your transmit power level does not require a formal assessment, you are not released from the requirement to

not expose people to excessive levels of RF. Second, your indoor receiving antenna will pick up electrical noise from other equipment in the building. Third, if the building contains any sensitive electronic systems, your signal has a good chance of causing trouble, such as setting off fire alarms, or getting in to a television receiver while a spouse is watching an important show. In any case, any radiation that occurs within the building structure is not likely to help you get your signal where you want it.

None of this is to suggest that indoor antennas can't be used, however all of the above issues need to be considered. Here we are talking about an antenna that is partly inside a building, and partly outside. The point is that having as much as possible outside is generally a better solution.

Antenna Tuner at the Antenna — The antenna tuner can also be located at the antenna, if it's remotely tuned or sometimes remotely switched. Some remote tuners are waterproof, while others will need a waterproof enclosure to make them last. With the tuner at or near the antenna feed point, matched coax can run from the tuner back to the station, as discussed previously. By running the coax from the station out to the antenna feed point, the issues of radiation within the building can be largely avoided.

This is the configuration used for

Table 13-1

Random Wire Antenna Lengths that Should be Avoided Due to Resonance and High Impedance.

Band (Meters)	0.5 λ	1 λ	1.5 λ	2 λ	2.5 λ	3 λ
160	234 to 260	468 to 520	702 to 780	936 to 1040	1170.0 to 1300.0	1404.0 to 1560.0
80	117.0 to 133.7	234.0 to 267.4	351.0 to 401.1	468.0 to 534.9	585.0 to 668.6	702.0 to 802.3
40	64.1 to 66.9	128.2 to 133.7	192.3 to 200.6	256.4 to 267.4	320.5 to 334.3	384.7 to 401.1
30	46.1 to 46.3	92.2 to 92.7	138.3 to 139.0	184.4 to 185.3	230.5 to 231.7	276.7 to 278.0
20	32.6 to 33.4	65.2 to 66.9	97.8 to 100.3	130.5 to 133.7	163.1 to 167.1	195.7 to 200.6
17	25.8 to 25.9	51.5 to 51.8	77.3 to 77.7	103.0 to 103.6	128.8 to 129.5	154.6 to 155.4
15	21.8 to 22.3	43.6 to 44.6	65.5 to 66.9	87.3 to 89.1	109.1 to 111.4	130.9 to 133.7
12	18.7 to 18.8	37.5 to 37.6	56.2 to 56.4	74.9 to 75.2	93.6 to 94.0	112.4 to 112.8
10	15.8 to 16.7	31.5 to 33.4	47.3 to 50.1	63.0 to 66.9	78.8 to 83.6	94.5 to 100.3
6	8.7 to 9.4	17.3 to 18.7	26.0 to 28.1	34.7 to 37.4	43.3 to 46.8	52.0 to 56.2

many marine HF antennas. On a sailboat, the typical HF antenna is an insulated backstay fed by a remote single wire tuner located near the antenna base and fed against the ship ground system, including salt water, if possible.

But Watch Out for Tricky Lengths! — The so called *random length* wire antenna is not really random since any antenna does have a specific length. Such an antenna will work better at some lengths than others, making it best if not entirely random in its installation. The problems most often show up if the length happens to be a multiple of $\lambda/2$. At this length, the impedance hits a maximum, often in the 1000 to 2000 Ω range, depending on the usual factors. This results in an SWR of 20 to 40:1, higher than even a wide range tuner promises to deal with.

The impedance gets somewhat lower with each multiple of a $\lambda/2$, but may still be a problem. A second concern is that the voltage on the end at the tuner is high. The voltage can be nearly 500 V_{RMS} with a 100 W transmitter. This can stress tuner capacitors as well as pose a safety hazard to unsuspecting people. Instead of the shock experienced by coming in contact with dc or 60 Hz ac, contact with RF results in a painful burn that is usually slow to heal.

While it sounds like it should be an easy task to select a length, the multiplicity of bands without harmonic relationship makes it difficult to find a length that won't be likely a problem on some band. A look at **Table 13-1**, indicating approximate $\lambda/2$ resonant lengths for each band, along with multiples, provides a list of lengths to avoid for the amateur bands. There are so few lengths available, that sometimes it makes sense to just try the length that fits the available spot and, if it has problems tuning on a band, add a few feet and try again.

The Vertical Monopole

A popular antenna with those who like to operate long distances on the lower HF and MF bands is a vertical monopole. This can perhaps be considered a special case of the random wire antenna, except that it is generally of specific electrical length — typically $\lambda/4$ or $\frac{5}{8}\lambda$, depending on frequency and available supports. While a $\lambda/4$ vertical monopole can usually be fed directly with 50 Ω coax against ground, the other lengths do require matching networks or an antenna tuner for operation with a transmission line. A low impedance ground is a requirement for efficient operation of such antennas.

A 43 foot tall vertical made from wire or tubing is a very popular antenna in some quarters. It is a $\frac{5}{8}\lambda$ long monopole on 20 meters and thus provides the optimum low angle radiation from a single vertical radiator (see **Figure 13-5**), yet can provide excellent low angle performance on 40 meters where it is somewhat longer than $\lambda/4$, as well as on 80 meters where it is somewhat less than $\lambda/4$, but generally a manageable height. All the lengths share a complex feed point impedance that responds

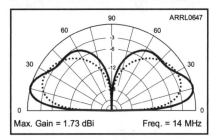

Figure 13-5 — Vertical radiation patterns of a 43 foot, $\frac{5}{8}\lambda$, vertical on 20 meters (solid) compared to a $\frac{1}{4}\lambda$ monopole. Note the increased radiation at low elevation angles.

nicely to a remote tuner at the base, although at these frequencies, a short run of high quality coax may have sufficiently low in loss to be suitable for use with a tuner at the station.

Inverted L

A popular variant of the vertical monopole, particularly on the lower frequency bands, is the inverted L. A $\lambda/4$ monopole for 160 meters, for example, needs to be around 130 feet long — a bit of a stretch for most as a vertical arrangement. The inverted L is obtained by taking the same length of wire and going as high as feasible, then bending the remainder horizontally. The antenna has the appearance of an upside down letter L — hence its name.

The lower (vertical) portion has the highest current and will thus provide low angle radiation very similar to that of a full sized monopole. At the $\lambda/4$ frequency, the inverted L can often be fed directly by 50 Ω coax with a reasonable SWR. An additional advantage of this arrangement, if fed with a wide range tuner at its base, is that it will provide low angle vertically polarized radiation at higher frequencies up to the frequency at which the vertical portion is just longer than $\frac{5}{8}\lambda$. Note the earlier concerns about feeding an antenna that is a multiple of $\lambda/2$, and if multiband operation is in the plan, make the inverted L longer than $\lambda/4$ on the lowest band.

The Bobtail Curtain

An interesting, inexpensive and surprisingly effective directional array called the Bobtail Curtain is composed of three $\lambda/4$ vertical elements fed in phase and driven from the single wire center element as shown

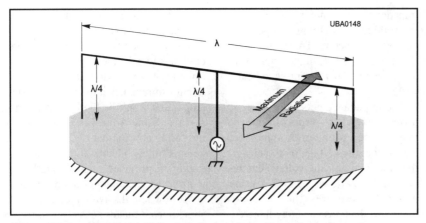

Figure 13-6 — The Bobtail Curtain three element vertical phased array fed by a single wire.

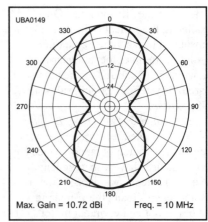

Figure 13-7 — Azimuth pattern of a Bobtail Curtain array at 10° elevation. Note the high gain over 60° on each side, broadside to the array.

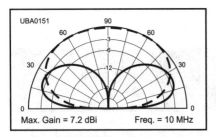

Figure 13-8 — Elevation pattern of a Bobtail Curtain array (solid) compared to a full wave center fed antenna on the same supports (dashed). Note the superior low angle coverage.

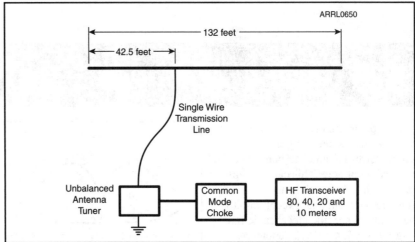

Figure 13-9 — Single wire fed Windom antenna configuration for 80, 40, 20 and 10 meters.

in **Figure 13-6.**[1] This antenna is composed of just four pieces of wire, yet provides significant gain in two fixed directions as shown in **Figure 13-7**. The low angle gain of this antenna favors long distance communication (see **Figure 13-8**) and is higher than that of horizontal antennas of the same height.

The Bobtail Curtain can be fed by a single wire tuner located at the source shown in Figure 13-6,

although the impedance is quite high, as discussed in the previous section. Making the middle wire a few feet longer may make it usable with most wide range tuners. The antenna can be used on other bands as a kind of top loaded monopole, although the results will not be in the same league as those at its design frequency.

Single Wire Fed Windom

An unbroken half wave antenna off-center fed by a single wire was quite a popular multiband radiator in the 1930s, following publication of a note by Windom in *QST*.[2] The Windom antenna, as shown in **Figure 13-9,** with a fundamental fre-

quency in the lower portion of 80 meters, was said to operate equally well on 40, 20 and 10 meters, thus covering all the amateur HF bands of the day.

There is some controversy over just how well this antenna works as a horizontal antenna; however, there is no question that it can work. Figure 13-9 shows a choke or current balun in the coax from the tuner to the radio, since there will likely be significant common mode current that should be kept out of the radio room.

[1]For more about the Bobtail Curtain array, see J. Hallas, W1ZR, *Basic Antennas — Understanding Practical Antennas and Designs,* Chapter 15. Available from your ARRL dealer or the ARRL Bookstore, ARRL order no. 9994. Telephone 860-594-0355, or toll-free in the US 888-277-5289; **www.arrl.org/shop/; pubsales@arrl.org**.

[2]L. Windom, W8GZ, "Notes on Ethereal Adornments," *QST,* Sep 1929, pp 19-22, 84.

Balanced Antenna Systems

For many amateurs, the antenna tuner really earns its keep by matching balanced systems for multiple bands. The classic system is one that is often called a center-fed Zepp, although there are some who suggest it really should have different names on different bands.

The Center-Fed Zepp

This antenna is actually a half-wave dipole if fed on its lowest band. The difference between it and the usual dipole is that it is fed with low-loss balanced transmission line, such as open wire line or window type line. Since it doesn't really need to be resonant to work well, and thus can be almost any length, a more accurate name might be the *not always resonant tuned feeder dipole*. Still more folk will know what you mean if you call it a center-fed Zepp (CFZ). The configuration is shown in **Figure 13-10**.

For the case in which it is resonant at its half wave frequency, the radiation pattern is the same as any half-wave dipole at the same height. The difference is that the SWR on the transmission line will be in the range of 4:1 to 10:1 depending on the height of the antenna and the transmission line type. While the loss with this kind of mismatch would be a problem with coax, it isn't with low loss line. Including the loss due to mismatch, the total loss is comparable or even less than most matched coax situations at the same frequency.

The antenna can easily be fed with a wide range antenna tuner, preferably a balanced antenna tuner, but usually also with an unbalanced tuner equipped with a balun. The antenna will work very well on higher bands — into the VHF range. There may be some lengths of transmission line that will result in an impedance that the tuner can deal with on all bands.

The antenna patterns become fairly complex at higher frequencies. For resonant antennas, there are generally 2 × N main lobes where N is the number of full wavelengths.

As mentioned, the antenna has no particular need to be resonant anywhere to work well. The impedance is easier to match if the antenna is at least a half wave long at its lowest frequency, but there is nothing magic about that length. I use a 100 foot long dipole, center fed with 450 Ω window line quite successfully on all bands from 80 through 6 meters, for example.

Another popular length is 86 feet. This provides the optimum gain on 20 meters in single lobes in each direction perpendicular to the wire. While the lobes are sharp compared to a dipole, 35.6° on either side compared to 83°, the gain at the peak is more than 3 dB higher than a dipole.

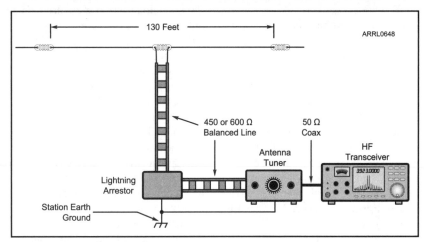

Figure 13-10 — Traditional center-fed Zepp antenna. With the length shown, the antenna will work well from 80 through 6 meters, and may even tune on 160 meters. The antenna length is not critical, however, it works best if close to λ/2 on the lowest operating frequency as described in the text.

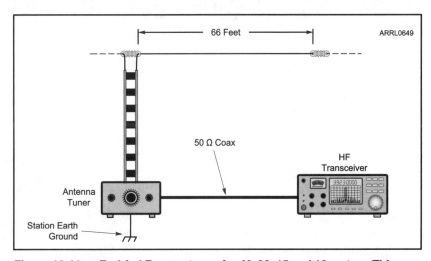

Figure 13-11 — End-fed Zepp antenna for 40, 20, 15 and 10 meters. This works as a horizontal antenna if the length is a multiple of λ/2 on each frequency used. On other frequencies the feed line will also radiate, usually with vertical polarization, and precautions must be taken to keep common mode currents from the radio equipment. Lightning arrestor not shown.

This length will usually be useable from 80 meters through the higher frequency bands, although some transmission line lengths may have problems with some wide range tuners on 80 meters.

If there are problems matching particular impedances, usually an extra 10 feet or so of the transmission line will change the impedance enough to make the match possible. Be sure to check the other bands to make sure you haven't just moved the problem around. Usually a length can be found that will work on all bands. Be sure to avoid coiling up the excess balanced line. Always keep it off the ground and away from metal — at least three or four times the distance between the conductors.

The End-Fed Zepp

A half wave antenna fed on the end with a λ/4 matching section of low loss balanced line is called an end-fed Zepp. This is often a convenient antenna if the station is close to a property boundary, making a center-fed antenna a difficult proposition. The matching section transforms the high impedance on the end, typically close to 2000 Ω, to a relatively low impedance that can be fed by a transmitter, or a narrow range tuner. This is the original Zeppelin antenna that was deployed beneath the aircraft's gondola. It is also popular as a VHF vertical called a "J-antenna."

Some have had better results by providing a λ/10 or so of wire as a counterpoise on the other side of the transmission line, particularly if using it on multiple bands. On bands at which the antenna is a multiple of λ/2, it provides mostly horizontal polarization with minimal common mode current on the transmission line. It can be made to work on bands at which it is not resonant, however, there will be a pronounced lack of balance on the transmission line.

While the λ/4 matching section is a key part of the original Zepp design, it is not necessary if a wide range antenna tuner is provided to perform the matching as shown in **Figure 13-11**.

The unbalanced line currents result in two effects.

• First, the line will radiate. This may not be a terrible thing, if the line is in the clear, but can cause problems if it is running near other equipment.

• Second, the line will bring common mode current into the station. This can usually be addressed through a common mode choke at the point at which a transition to coax is made. Make sure the coax run is short, since the mismatch will result in much higher losses in coax.

Mobile Antenna Systems

Antennas used in vehicles operate under the same principles as antennas in other applications, however, they often provide unique challenges. Antennas for MF and the lower portion of the HF region must be shortened considerably in order to be practical on most motor vehicles, large ships are a notable exception. In addition, unlike the usual antenna environment, these antennas are usually quite close to both the radio equipment as well as the vehicle body. With the exception of aircraft antennas, most mobile antennas are also quite close to the ground.

While none of the above differences by itself results in major problems, they all lead to certain limitations in

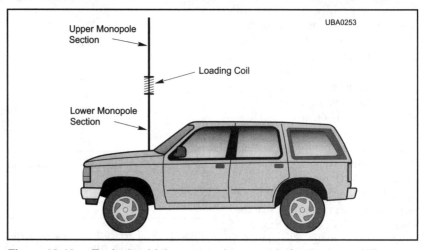

Figure 13-12 — Typical vehicle mounted monopole for the lower HF range. Because of practical limitations to do with garages, tunnels and trees, lengths tend to be 8 feet or less, from about ⅛ to ¹⁄₃₂ wavelength. The center loading shown improves efficiency.

antenna design and performance.

HF Mobile Antennas on Land Vehicles

The lower HF bands, especially 80, 40 and 20 meters, are popular with mobile operators. Depending on the sunspots and time of day, one or more can usually be counted on for reliable medium to long range communication. The usual antenna is a relatively short monopole antenna mounted on, and fed against, the vehicle body as shown in **Figure 13-12**.

As in the antenna in Figure 13-12, center loading is often used because it results in higher current in the lower section and thus less loss, although base loading, or even just using a solid whip with a tuner at the base are often encountered. A limitation of such an antenna is its SWR bandwidth, a typical case shown in **Figure 13-13** — much narrower than a full size antenna.

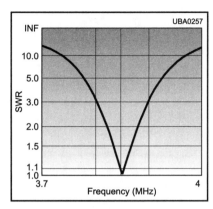

Figure 13-13 — Typical SWR plot of a mobile antenna of the type shown in Figure 13-12. The 2:1 SWR bandwidth is likely to range from 20 to 50 kHz, with antennas having less efficiency tending to have wider bandwidth.

This makes the shortened mobile antenna a good candidate for a wide range antenna tuner. The tuner can be used to allow full band coverage to be obtained. I have even used a tuner to allow a 40 meter mobile whip to be used on 80 meters, although it is not as efficient as the center loaded 80 meter arrangement.

HF Mobile Antennas on Other Vehicles

Those using HF on boats or aircraft do not generally share the same size restrictions as on land vehicles. Often either will use a convenient length of wire, for example the insulated backstay on a sailboat, or a wire from a short mast to a handy surface on an aircraft, to form an antenna similar to the random wire described earlier. This is almost always accompanied by a remote, usually automatic, antenna tuner very near one end or the other of the wire. This system can work very well if fed against the aircraft body or a metal hull. On my fiberglass sailboat, I feed it against the ship ground system.

Review Questions

13-1 Under what circumstances can an antenna tuner be of benefit in feeding a simple coax fed λ/2 dipole?

13-2 Why is it important to use low-loss transmission line such as window or ladder line if using a dipole on multiple bands?

13-3 What are the possible consequences of common mode currents on a transmission line?

Chapter 14

A Survey of Available Tuners

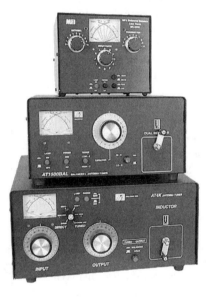

A selection of modern balanced antenna tuners on the left with a 1950s John Matchbox tuner.

Contents

Key Tuner Paramaters

Virtually every configuration of antenna tuner, capable of operation at every legal power level, is available commercially from one or more vendors. This can make selecting a commercial tuner a bit of a challenge, just as it is much tougher to select a meal from a restaurant with many good choices, compared to just a few.

Fortunately, the choices can be quickly reduced if one can make a few decisions on key tuner parameters. I will try to organize them in a way that will help make the selection easier. The following are the major decisions to be made, in this person's opinion:

What Frequencies Do You Want the Tuner to Cover?

When talking about antenna tuners, we almost always are talking about the HF range, although there are also some tuners for VHF bands. This means that we want to cover the amateur bands from 80 through 10 meters — that's a *given*. Most current amateur transceivers also cover 160 meters. Is that of interest? If so, because it often doubles the size of many tuner components, it will likely add significantly to the cost and size of a tuner, all other things being equal. The 160 meter band is gaining in popularity since it provides interesting operational conditions at the bottom of the sunspot cycle, as I write this. If you have room for effective 160 meter antennas, having a tuner that supports operation here may be a good choice.

On the other end of the spectrum is 6 meters. More and more current amateur "HF" transceiver cross into operation on our lowest VHF band. This band is also quite popular now since there are long distance modes that don't depend on sunspot activity. If you have, or expect to have, a dedicated 6 meter antenna, the chances are that it will be suitable to be fed directly with 50 Ω coax and a tuner will not be needed. On the other

hand, if you will need to use your all band tuner fed antenna, such as the center-fed Zepp, on this band, you will want to include that capability in your tuner.

The other frequency decisions may be more subtle. Operation on 10 meters is sometimes a problem with larger tuners that have trouble ending up with sufficiently low minimum inductance and capacitance to provide the same impedance coverage on 10 meters as on the other bands — check the specifications to get an idea. In a similar vein, some tuners don't have quite enough maximum inductance or capacitance to provide the tuning capability to cover 80 (or 160) meters with the same range as on the other bands.

How Much Power Do You Expect to Run?

For any given tuner design, there is no factor that influences tuner cost and size more than power level. This should not be a surprise since higher power means higher voltage and current stress on the components within. The obvious answer might be to pick a tuner with a power rating equal to the most power that your transmitter can put out — but be careful, there are four issues hidden here:

• The power rating is based on the manufacturer's SWR specification (if they did a proper design job). If it says a tuner is good for an SWR of 10:1, typical for a wide range tuner, and you tune an antenna with a 20:1 SWR, you may be able to get a match, but either the voltage or the current in the tuner can be higher by a factor of $\sqrt{(20/10)}$, or 1.41 times. That may explain the arcing, or the burning smell, you observe on some frequencies! The answer may be to go somewhat higher in power rating than you expect to actually run.

• So you now have that shiny new 100 W transceiver — you love it to death and can't imagine that you will

ever need more power. You buy a 100 W antenna tuner (or better a 200 W tuner, as discussed above) and happily make many contacts with your stealthy antenna. Now you decide to try for DXCC and notice that the DXpedition in Outer Slovenia can almost hear you, but can't quite copy your call letters. A bigger antenna is out of the question — the only solution is a high power amplifier. Oops, now you have an almost new 100 W tuner that you can no longer use.

• In addition to taking up more space, and more lawnmowing money, high power tuners often, because of the physical size of the components, have trouble providing the tuning range some antennas need on the higher bands. Some switch out portions of the circuit on higher bands to avoid the problem, but some don't. Keep your eye on that ball, if looking at higher power tuners.

• On the plus side, higher power tuners usually have inductors that are wound with heavier wire. This reduces losses, although it may not be noticeable in the test results.

Do You Want a Balanced or Unbalanced Tuner?

If you expect to be feeding single wire or coax-fed antennas, an unbalanced antenna tuner will be fine. If you want to feed an antenna such as a center fed Zepp with balanced line, you will need to have some provision to feed a balanced load. This can be handled in one of three ways:

• A fully balanced tuner is ideally suited to matching to balanced loads within its matching range. These are available in multiple power ranges and can work quite well. A disadvantage of these is that many do not include all the switching options of many unbalanced tuners — not a problem if you expect to use a single antenna.

• Many inherently unbalanced

tuners include an output connection through an internal balun. These work best with balanced loads within about 4:1 SWR of the balun design impedance. Most use 4:1 baluns designed for a 200 Ω load. That means they will work reasonably well with resistive loads from 50 to 800 Ω, and with complex loads of a similar SWR. They will also work outside that range, although their response can be a bit unpredictable. If they don't get hot, they are probably putting the power where you want it.

•The same kind of balun can be added outside of an unbalanced tuner if you decide to move from coax to a balanced feeder system. The same concerns as noted above apply. However there are some advantages such as that you can custom design the balun for the impedance that each antenna has, and you can have the balun some distance from the station equipment — but watch out for mismatched coax losses if the distance is more than a few feet.

Do Your Want a Remote or Local Tuner?

An antenna tuner that is located next to the radio in the station area offers a lot of plusses in terms of control and monitoring. Some antennas, however, really want the impedance matching performed at the antenna. A big consideration here is that if the tuner is located with the antenna, it usually can only operate with that single antenna, although remote switching is possible. If the antenna tuner is near the radio,

switching between antennas systems is usually much easier — sometimes provided within the tuner, sometimes outside — but always within reach.

Do you Want a Manual or an Automatic Tuner?

A manual tuner requires adjusting two or three controls (and often switches) every time either frequency is changed, typically by around 50 kHz, depending on what band is selected or what type antenna is used. The adjustments can be tedious, although recording them makes returning to a proper tune under previously encountered conditions fairly easy.

An automatic tuner, on the other hand, just requires a push of the button to obtain a tune. Many have some sort of memory arrangement so they can quickly return to previous settings. The tuning usually takes a few seconds the first time, a fraction thereafter. While it is possible to imagine a remote manual tuner, to my knowledge, all remote tuners are of the automatic flavor. So if you want remote, you get automatic.

The idea of an automatic tuner sounds pretty good, and it is. There are just a few items to be aware of, as noted below:

•In general, an auto tuner will make a match within its specified SWR threshold, often 1.5:1, but check and compare with your radio's requirement. With your manual tuner, you can usually find a 1:1 setting. If the radio will put out its full power into the load, this is not

worth worrying about.

•Watch out for tuners that initiate a tune on their own. Some can be just *too* automatic to suit me. You tune your radio 25 kHz off your previous frequency to capture a neat DX station, start to call, and hear your antenna tuner relays clacking. Chances are the up and down tuning will result in the station missing some part of your call sign.

Of more concern, if there is no circuitry to prevent it, many automatic tuners that can handle 100 W, for example, want tuning to occur at a lower power level to avoid burning relay contacts. If it starts up while you are operating, you can easily hit it at full power before you know what's happening. In the mobile environment, this can also happen as you pass that 18 wheeler with a giant piece of aluminum detuning your antenna (it can also serve as a reflector, if you get it in the right place!).

•I once thought that the small components in the usual compact automatic antenna tuner would result in more losses compared to the larger components, especially inductors, in the usual manual tuners. To my surprise, following the test results presented below, this does not seem to be the case, although it might be buried in the 5% minimum loss, below which we don't report due to measurement uncertainty. If it is a loss of that level (0.2 dB), in my opinion, it should not be part of the decision process.

Product Review Testing

The American Radio Relay League (ARRL), the US Amateur Radio organization publishes a monthly magazine, *QST*, for its members. In addition to its many technical and general interest features, each month's issue includes detailed reviews of products of interest to its readers. These Product Reviews generally include laboratory evaluation of equipment operational parameters using professional grade, independently calibrated test instruments. Over the years, we have had many such reviews of antenna tuners and I have reproduced the results from some here.

While many of the reviews include currently available equipment, some models covered are no longer available as new equipment. Even so, it may be of benefit in two ways:

• There is an active used equipment market in Amateur Radio equipment. This may provide a way to knowledgeably purchase an antenna tuner at a lower cost.

• In some cases, manufacturers have made relatively small changes to equipment, so data on previous models may be directly applicable.

ARRL Lab Antenna Tuner Testing Methodology

The following method was used in the ARRL Lab to measure the loss of the tuners presented below. Two test fixtures were built which would hold combinations of high power 50 Ω "non-inductive" carbon resistors (one fixture for parallel combinations and one for series), one shown in **Figure 14-1**. Even with the non-inductive resistors, some net fixture inductance was apparent at some frequencies, so a variable capacitor was used to compensate. The fixture accuracy was measured using the Lab's vector impedance meter.

Each fixture used an input connection (for the tuner) and an output connection. The output connection went to a 50 Ω input power attenuator, which took the place of one of the resistors in the load (for the series loads, it was always the one on the ground side of the network). The output of the power attenuator was connected to a high accuracy laboratory wattmeter, and the actual attenuation was measured for each frequency. The tuners were matched

at low power, then 100 W of RF was applied at the input, with the output being measured by the Lab's wattmeter.

Each tuner was connected to the load fixture at each resistive impedance level for testing in the ARRL Lab. A 100 W RF source fed the input of the tuner. The resistive load was connected to the antenna output. The load was connected to a 50 Ω. power attenuator, which took the place of the final resistors. This is a close-up of the parallel load test fixture. The variable capacitor was used to compensate for fixture inductance encountered at some frequencies. While complex impedance loads could have been tested as well, the additional data points would have made testing impractical. We believe that the results at a particular SWR should be representative of other loads with the same SWR.

Note that the reviews were conducted over a period of a few years and the data taken, as well as the presentation, varied slightly from review to review. Please make sure that you are comparing equivalent data.

Figure 14-1 — Close up of test figure used to test antenna tuner efficiency into loads from 50 Ω down using paralleled 50 Ω noninductive loads.

QST Reviews Five High Power Antenna Tuners

Reviewed by Jim Parise, W1UK
ARRL Technical Advisor
QST *February, 2003*

One piece of gear that finds its way into most everyone's shack at one time or another is an HF antenna tuner. First of all, the name antenna tuner is something of a misnomer. It does not tune the antenna at all, but acts as an impedance transformer that provides your transmitting equipment with the proper load, usually 50 Ω.

Who needs an antenna tuner? Well, anyone who has the need to match an antenna with an impedance outside the range of their transmitter or amplifier's output circuits. Modern transceivers often have built-in tuners that are capable of matching SWR mismatches up to 3:1. Beyond that they need help, and if you use an amplifier you most surely will need one. Many hams find themselves with limited antenna choices and the desire to operate on frequencies other than

what they were designed for, or use non-resonant multiband antennas that require a tuner. The five HF tuners we tested are all in the kilowatt class, meaning the manufacturer rates their power handling capability at 1 kW output or more.

With the wide range of frequencies in the HF spectrum and the huge diversity of antenna types in use, tuners are expected to perform under an incredible number of possible combinations. Some are more efficient at it than others. A measure of a tuner's ability to transform impedances efficiently is energy loss. Under extreme conditions a tuner can get quite hot or arc over at power levels well under the manufacturers rating. Heat in a tuner is a product of loss. RF energy being dissipated as heat is lost power that will not find its way to your antenna and onto the air.

Tuner losses generally get higher as the impedance of the load decreas-

es. If a ham were running 1500 W into a tuner that was 50% efficient, 750 W would be dissipated in the tuner. Most of the loss in a tuner occurs in the coil, and no coil can withstand 750 W of power. A high-power tuner could probably be safely used at 50% efficiency and 100 W, but hams should be careful with high SWR and high power, or a tuner failure is a real possibility. Each tuner was tested into resistive impedances that ranged from 6.25 to 400 Ω, and their respective percentage of loss and 1.5 SWR bandwidth measured. The tuners were also used in everyday communications on all bands at power levels up to 1 kW, matching a G5RV fed with balanced ladder line and a 160 meter inverted L fed with coax.

The characteristicvs of the five uners tested are described in **Table 14-1**. Each tuner is described separately below.

Table 14-1
Comparison of Five Antenna Tuners

	Ameritron ATR-30	MFJ MFJ-986	Palstar AT1500 CV	Ten-Tec 238A	Vectronics HFT-1500
Circuit Type	T-network	T-network	T-network	L-network	T-network
SWR/wattmeter	Cross-needle	Cross-needle	Cross-needle	Single-needle	Cross-needle
Balun type	4:1 current	4:1 current	4:1 voltage	4:1voltage	4:1 voltage
Manufacturer's claimed PEP rating	3000 W	3000 W	1500 W	2000 W	2000 W
Manufacturer's claimed Matching range	35-500	35-500	20-1500	5-3000	Not specified
Physical dimensions (HWD) in inches	5.25×13×14.4	4.1×11×15.2	4.5×12.5×12	5.5×13×11	5.5×12.5×12

AMERITRON ATR-30

The ATR-30 (**Figures 14-2**, **3**, **4**) is Ameritron's legal limit T-network antenna tuner offering. It is housed in a plain, all black aluminum enclosure with a scratch resistant coated front panel. A look under the cover reveals two large variable capacitors and an air core edge wound silver plated roller inductor. Like most of the other tuners reviewed here, the capacitors are adjusted with vernier reduction drives, and although they tune smoothly, they require a lot of force to turn. The roller inductor is adjusted with a plastic lever type knob and is quite stiff to crank. The roller itself is a pinch roller, and the physical resistance in turning the crank may be offset by lessoned contact resistance.

The balun is constructed with three large cores and wound with wire covered with Teflon tubing. The cross-needle meter displays both average and peak power in switchable 300 W or 3 kW ranges. The wattmeter requires dc to function. It is illuminated by either a 12 V barrel connector on the back panel or a 9 V battery accessible through a trap door on the bottom of the unit. With 12 V, both the meter and inductor turns counter are illuminated. When a 9 V battery is used, the meter will function, but the panel lamps will not light.

Finding a match on 80 meters on the G5RV required quite a bit of time finding the right combination of capacitor tuning and inductance, and the stiff controls didn't make it much fun. Finding the sweet spot on the higher bands was much easier. There are three coax outputs on the ATR-30, including two that may be switched direct or through the T-network and a third direct only. Single or balanced

feed lines connect to large ceramic binding posts with wing nuts. Test results are summarized in **Table 14-2**.

Manufacturer: Ameritron, 116 Willow Rd, Starkville, MS 39759; tel 662-323-8211; fax 662-323-6551; **www.ameritron.com**. 2003 price: $599.95.

Table 14-2
Ameritron ATR-30 Loss and Bandwidth Test Results

SWR	Load (Ω)		160 m	80 m	40 m	20 m	10 m
8:1	6.25	Power Loss %	20	12	<10	<10	<10
		1.5 SWR BW	1	3	>5	4	>5
4.1	12.5	Power Loss %	15	<10	<10	<10	<10
		1.5 SWR BW	3	4	>5	>5	>5
2:1	25	Power Loss %	10	<10	<10	<10	<10
		1.5 SWR BW	4	>5	>5	>5	>5
1:1	50	Power Loss %	<10	<10	<10	<10	<10
		1.5 SWR BW	>5	>5	>5	>5	>5
2:1	100	Power Loss %	<10	<10	<10	<10	<10
		1.5 SWR BW	>5	>5	>5	>5	>5
4:1	200	Power Loss %	<10	<10	<10	<10	<10
		1.5 SWR BW	>5	>5	>5	>5	5
8:1	400	Power Loss %	<10	<10	<10	<10	<10
		1.5 SWR BW	>5	>5	>5	>5	3

Notes
Power losses are expressed as a percentage. A 21% loss of power is 1 dB.
The 1.5-SWR Bandwidth (SWR BW) represents the bandwidth over which an SWR of 1.5:1 or less was maintained as a percentage of the measurement frequencies (1.8, 3.5, 7.2, 14.2 and 29.7 MHz).

Figure 14-3 — Interior circuitry of the Ameritron ATR-30.

Figure 14-2 — Front panel of the Ameritron ATR-30.

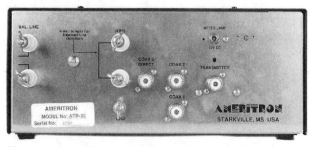

Figure 14-4 — Rear panel connections on the Ameritron ATR-30.

MFJ-986

The '986 is one of more than 20 antenna tuner products offered by the prolific MFJ (in 2003). It is rated for 1500 W PEP within the 35-500 Ω impedance range, positioning it alongside the '989C as one of their high power units. Unlike the traditional T-network with a pair of variable capacitors, the '986 (**Figures 14-5, 6, 7**)makes use of a single variable capacitor and a wire wound air core roller inductor with a three digit turns counter. The tuner uses what MFJ describes as a "differential" capacitor. It has two discrete sets of fixed plates and one variable set, with a single capacitor control, forming a T-network with the inductor.

The cabinet is narrow and extends nearly 18 inches deep. The cross-needle meter has a high (3000 W) and low (300 W) setting switched by a front panel button, and it can display average and peak power as well as SWR. Providing 12 V to the connector on the back panel brightly illuminates the meter. Both the capacitor and roller inductor are directly driven. The inductance knob has a finger depression, which are often found on a transceiver's tuning knob. It is somewhat awkward to turn due to binding. The tuner had a tendency to creep around the operating desk when the inductor is rapidly turned. A check inside revealed several loose screws holding the inductor to the chassis. Tightening these did improve the smoothness somewhat.

The '986 provided a match to both antennas quickly, but arced over on 80 meters with the inverted L at 900 W. While this tuner does provide ease of use, one should give careful consideration to the loss figures in the tables. During operation the meter developed an intermittent problem with both needles going off scale even with very low power applied and a low SWR. Movement of the SWR bridge

circuit board on the inside back panel seemed to correct the problem.

Two coax outputs are provided that can be switched to bypass the tuning circuit, as well as a third output for a dummy load. Balanced and single-wire feed lines connect to large ceramic feed through posts with wing

nuts. A 4:1 two-core current balun is provided at the output. Test results are summarized in **Table 14-3**.

Manufacturer: MFJ Enterprises, Inc, PO Box 494, Mississippi State, MS 39762; tel 800-647-1800; fax 662-323-6551; **www.mfjenterprises.com**. 2003 price: $329.95.

Table 14-3
MFJ-986 Loss and Bandwidth Test Results

SWR	Load (Ω)		160 m	80 m	40 m	20 m	10 m
8:1	6.25	Power Loss %	47	31	21	16	13
		1.5 SWR BW	1	1	2	4	>5
4.1	12.5	PowerLoss %	33	22	14	12	11
		1.5 SWR BW	1	1	4	5	>5
2:1	25	PowerLoss %	25	20	10	<10	10
		1.5 SWR BW	1	2	4	>5	>5
1:1	50	PowerLoss %	22	12	<10	<10	<10
		1.5 SWR BW	2	3	>5	>5	>5
2:1	100	PowerLoss %	15	10	<10	<10	19
		1.5 SWR BW	3	5	>5	>5	>5
4:1	200	PowerLoss %	11	<10	<10	<10	<10
		1.5 SWR BW	3	>5	>5	>5	>5
8:1	400	PowerLoss %	10	<10	<10	11	16
		1.5 SWR BW	3	>5	>5	>5	5

Notes
Power losses are expressed as a percentage. A 21% loss of power is 1 dB.
The 1.5-SWR Bandwidth (SWR BW) represents the bandwidth over which an SWR of 1.5:1 or less was maintained as a percentage of the measurement frequencies (1.8, 3.5, 7.2, 14.2 and 29.7 MHz).

Figure 14-6 — Interior circuitry of the MFJ-986.

Figure 14-5 — Front panel of the MFJ-986.

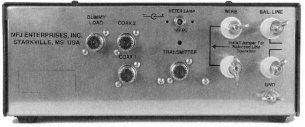

Figure 14-7 — Rear panel connections on the MFJ-986.

PALSTAR AT1500CV

The Palstar AT1500CV (**Figures 14-8, 9, 10**) is a T-network tuner solidly constructed in a compact aluminum enclosure. Inside, the metering and SWR bridge circuitry are encased in their own aluminum boxes. The moderately sized variable capacitors are mounted side by side and feature large calibrated dials and silky smooth vernier tuning that allows for precise adjustment. Palstar indicates that newer units incorporate a roller bearing assembly which makes inductor adjustment smoother. The roller inductor is quite large. It is an air core silver plated edge wound coil with heavy-duty ceramic forms. Control of the inductor is via a lever handle and mechanical turns counter. It is not as smooth as some of the other tuners and tends to lurch as it is rotated during fine adjustments. The cross-needle meter displays SWR and average forward and reflected power in 300 and 3000 W ranges, with no option for peak power metering. It is illuminated with 12 V from an included wall adapter.

Achieving a 1:1 SWR on the G5RV was possible on all bands from 80 through 10 meters at its rated power maximum of 1000 W single tone. Similar results were noted on the inverted L. Although the tuning chart provided in the manual does not include settings for 30 meters, the tuner easily matched both antennas on that band. This tuner has a solid feel to it and doesn't creep around while making adjustments.

In laboratory tests, the AT1500CV had more difficulties on 160 meters than on other bands. A 1:1 SWR was only obtainable with the 25 and 50 Ω loads, the power losses at 160 meters were measurably greater than those on other bands at the same loads. The

variable capacitors are 240 pF maximum, which explains the 160 meter performance. The tradeoff results in lighter weight.

Antenna connections on the back panel include three coax inputs. Two are available direct or through the tuning network and one is bypassed

Table 14-4
Palstar AT1500CV Loss and Bandwidth Test Results

SWR	Load (Ω)		160 m	80 m	40 m	20 m	10 m
8:1	6.25	Power Loss %	No Match	25	16	12	12
		1.5 SWR BW		1	2	>5	3
4.1	12.5	Power Loss %	No Match	16	13	<10	11
		1.5 SWR BW		2	4	>5	>5
2:1	25	Power Loss %	21	13	<10	<10	<10
		1.5 SWR BW	2	3	>5	>5	>5
1:1	50	Power Loss %	13	<10	<10	<10	<10
		1.5 SWR BW	3	>5	>5	>5	>5
2:1	100	Power Loss %	No Match	<10	<10	<10	13
		1.5 SWR BW		>5	>5	>5	>5
4:1	200	Power Loss %	No Match	<10	<10	<10	12
		1.5 SWR BW		>5	>5	>5	>5
8:1	400	Power Loss %	No Match	<10	<10	<10	<10
		1.5 SWR BW		>5	>5	>5	5

Notes
"No Match" means that a 1:1 SWR could not be obtained.
Power losses are expressed as a percentage. A 21% loss of power is 1 dB.
The 1.5 SWR Bandwidth (SWR BW) represents the bandwidth over which an SWR of
   1.5:1 or less was maintained as a

Figure 14-10 — Interior circuitry of the Palstar AT1500CV.

Figure 14-8 — Front panel of the Palstar AT1500CV.

Figure 14-9 — Rear panel connections on the Palstar AT1500CV.

straight through. The bypass output can also be used with an optional 4:1 balun available for $39.95 [2003]. Balanced or single wire feed lines are attached to Delrin terminal posts with wing nuts.

Longer threaded material on the terminal posts would be a welcome improvement and make attachment of larger gauge wire much easier. In one isolated circumstance during lab testing, our engineer felt an RF bite on 10 meters through the metal portion of the inductor crank. This did not seem to be a pervasive problem, and Palstar indicates that the grounding on the crank has also recently been improved. Test results are summarized in Table 14-4.

Manufacturer: Palstar, Inc, 9676 N Looney Rd, PO Box 1136, Piqua, OH 45356; tel 937-773-6255; fax 937-773-8003; **www.palstarinc.com**. 2003 price: $429.95, optional 4:1 balun $39.95.

TEN-TEC 238A

The Ten-Tec 238A (**Figures 14-11, 12** and **13**) is the only tuner in our roundup to utilize an L-network. Using an innovative switching arrangement, the '238A actually provides five different circuit configurations to maximize efficiency. A look at the low loss figures in the table confirms this. The well-constructed tuner makes use of a single variable capacitor and a smooth turning wire-wound roller inductor to match impedances up to 3000 Ω. Additional capacitance can be switched into the circuit by means of a front panel switch. Five settings each are available for high and low impedances, as well as a bypass choice. A ceramic feed through post on the back panel provides a connection to add an additional 1000 pF capacitor (included with the tuner) to the circuit for matching 160 meter antennas. The small dual use meter can be switched to display SWR or RF power in either a 2000 or 200 W range. The meter lamp is powered by 12 V on the back panel.

The '238A handily matched all bands on both test antennas at full legal limit power. On 10 meters using the G5RV, the capacitor and inductor controls were a bit sensitive to small adjustments. One minor complaint: Measuring forward power in the high power range on the meter caused the indicator to slap the right extreme position during CW keying.

In laboratory tests, the '238A did not match on 160 meters into a 6.25 Ω until 2700 pF of external capacitance was added. Ten-Tec indicates they will provide additional capacitors to purchasers at no extra charge. Also, the power losses on 10 meters were considerably greater than those on other bands. However, the '238A performed very admirably on most other bands, quite often exhibiting the least losses on given band and load combinations.

Figure 14-13 — Interior circuitry of the Ten-Tec 238A.

Figure 14-11 — Front panel of the Ten-Tec 238A.

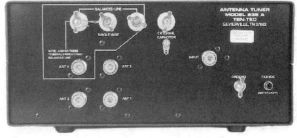

Figure 14-12 — Rear panel connections on the Ten-Tec 238A.

Table 14-5
Ten-Tec 238A Loss and Bandwidth Test Results

SWR	Load (Ω)		160 m	80 m	40 m	20 m	10 m
8:1	6.25	Power Loss %	No Match	<10	<10	<10	28
		1.5 SWR BW		>5	>5	>5	2
4.1	12.5	Power Loss %	<10	10	<10	<10	22
		1.5 SWR BW	>5	>5	>5	>5	2
2:1	25	Power Loss %	<10	10	<10	<10	17
		1.5 SWR BW	>5	>5	>5	>5	3
1:1	50	Power Loss %	<10	<10	<10	<10	<10
		1.5 SWR BW	>5	>5	>5	>5	>5
2:1	100	Power Loss %	<10	<10	<10	<10	20
		1.5 SWR BW	>5	>5	>5	>5	4
4:1	200	Power Loss %	<10	<10	<10	<10	20
		1.5 SWR BW	>5	>5	>5	>5	4
8:1	400	Power Loss %	<10	<10	<10	10	13
		1.5 SWR BW	>5	>5	>5	>5	1

Notes
"No Match" means that a 1:1 SWR could not be obtained, even with the included 1000 pF external capacitor attached. A match on 160 m at 6.25 was achieved with 2700 pF of external capacitance; the power loss was less than 10%, and the 1.5 SWR BW was greater than 5%.
Power losses are expressed as a percentage. A 21% loss of power is 1 dB. The 1.5-SWR Bandwidth (SWR BW) represents the bandwidth over which an SWR of 1.5:1 or less was maintained as a percentage of the measurement frequencies (1.8, 3.5, 7.2, 14.2 and 29.7 MHz).

The four-position antenna switch on the front panel allows selection of four coax outputs or a balanced/random wire. The balanced output and one coax connector share position four. A two-core balun is provided for matching the balanced output. The '238A is the only one of the five tuners reviewed here without an air-core inductor. The inductor here has a linen phenolic core.

Since we purchased our review unit, Ten-Tec has produced a substantially identical antenna tuner, the '238B. The Tennessee manufacturer is now selling only the '238B model. Test results are summarized in **Table 14-5**.

Manufacturer: Ten-Tec, 1185 Dolly Parton Pky, Sevierville, TN 37862; tel 865-453-7172; fax 865-428-4483; **www.tentec.com**. 2003 price: $475.00 ('238B).

VECTRONICS HFT-1500

The first thing you notice about the HFT-1500 (**Figures 14-14**, **15** and **16**) is the LED bar graph on the front panel that is used to display relative peak forward power. The bright green bar graph is adjusted to its maximum scale with a level control on the front panel to a known forward power reading on the cross-needle wattmeter. While it doesn't show actual power readings, it does give a quick visual indication of peak power. The cross-needle meter displays only average power and SWR in two power ranges selected by a pushbutton switch.

The traditional T-network design uses two 4.5 kV variable capacitors adjusted with large comfortable

Figure 14-16 — Interior circuitry of the VECTRONICS HFT-1500.

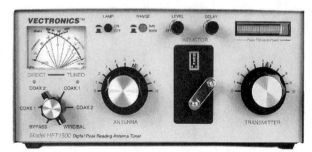

Figure 14-14 — Front panel of the VECTRONICS HFT-1500.

Figure 14-15 — Rear panel connections on the VECTRONICS HFT-1500.

Table 14-6
Vectronics HFT-1500 Loss and Bandwidth Test Results

SWR	Load (Ω)		160 m	80 m	40 m	20 m	10 m
8:1	6.25	Power Loss %	45	42	16	15	8
		1.5 SWR BW	1	<1	2	5	>5
4.1	12.5	Power Loss %	32	31	11	<10	<10
		1.5 SWR BW	>5	>5	3	>5	>5
2:1	25	Power Loss %	19	24	<10	<10	<10
		1.5 SWR BW	2	1	>5	>5	>5
1:1	50	Power Loss %	12	<10	<10	<10	<10
		1.5 SWR BW	3	>5	>5	>5	>5
2:1	100	Power Loss %	12	<10	<10	<10	<10
		1.5 SWR BW	3	>5	>5	>5	>5
4:1	200	Power Loss %	<10	<10	<10	<10	<10
		1.5 SWR BW	4	>5	>5	>5	>5
8:1	400	Power Loss %	<10	<10	<10	11	16
		1.5 SWR BW	4	>5	>5	>5	4

Notes
Power losses are expressed as a percentage. A 21% loss of power is 1 dB.
The 1.5-SWR Bandwidth (SWR BW) represents the bandwidth over which an SWR of
1.5:1 or less was maintained as a percentage of the measurement frequencies (1.8,
3.5, 7.2, 14.2 and 29.7 MHz).

knobs and very smooth vernier tuning. This tuner stays put on the desk while you utilize a lever handle and gear driven five digit mechanical turns counter to adjust the air wound roller inductor.

Tuning the 160-meter inverted L and the G5RV on all bands except 10 meters was easily accomplished, with no problems handling 1 kW. In the field, the best SWR that could be obtained on 10 was 2.33:1;

this is possibly due to the additional "loading" when a human touches the all-metal inductor crank. The ARRL Lab adjusted the inductor with a wooden pencil in some cases to obtain a match.

The HFT-1500 provides two coax inputs and a third that completely bypasses the tuning network. The balanced and single wire inputs are Delrin terminal posts connected to a large single core 4:1 voltage balun. In some circumstances during lab testing, our engineer felt RF bites through the metal portion of the inductor crank. Later units feature a metal shaft bushing that provides a better ground. This was not experienced in field testing, but tuner adjustments were not made at high power. Test results are summarized in **Table 14-6**.

Manufacturer: Vectronics, 300 Industrial Park Rd, Starkville MS 39759; tel 662-323-5800; fax 662-323-6551; **www.vectronics. com**. 2003 price: $459.95.

Automatic Antenna Tuners — A Sample of the Field

Reviewed by Joel R. Hallas, W1ZR
QST *Technical Editor*
QST *May, 2004*

Automatic antenna tuners can provide a quick and easy method of matching multiband or nonresonant antennas quickly and effortlessly. Performance is on par with manual tuners and there is now a selection available providing a fit to most requirements. A few years back, we surveyed the antenna tuner market in these pages. All those tuners were manual ones.

A few automatic tuners were available at that time, but they were the exception rather than the rule. Since then, a number of manufacturers have focused their attention on automatic antenna tuners and it seems as if there's now one for every application.

For this review we selected representative tuners from a number of manufacturers (see **Figure 14-17**). There are two general configurations: those providing remote tuning, with the tuner intended to be near the antenna, and those intended to be collocated with the station equipment. For those manufacturers having models in each camp, we selected one of each.

As noted in the specifications, each tuner is different and they don't exactly line up head-to-head, so a direct comparison is not always appropriate. Still, for each we will provide the basic data you would need to decide if one of these is a good fit for your needs. If you like the looks of a particular manufacturer, but the tuner reviewed doesn't exactly meet your requirements, check their Web page or your dealer for other models at different power levels or with different features.

For this review we stuck to those at the 100 to 200 W level and tried for a representative self-contained and remote tuner from each manufacturer. For these tests, we looked at units designed to work with any radio. In addition to these, most HF radio manufacturers offer external auto tuners designed to operate exclusively with their radios. One manufacturer, LDG, also offers tuners with the capabilities to operate with specific radios' commands. Many HF radio manufacturers also offer internal auto-tuners as a part of their transceivers. We generally review these as a part of the radios. We elected to stick to general purpose models for this review.

Those selected for this test include the RT-11 and Z-100 from LDG, the MFJ-991 and from SGC the SG-237 and MAC-200.

Remote vs Collocated Autotuners

It's probably worth a paragraph or two to discuss the relative merits and appropriateness of the two configura-

tions. If the antenna(s) to be matched terminate right at the station equipment, without a transmission line (or with a very short one), there is no particular advantage to having a remote tuner.

On the other hand, that setup often results in problems with "RF in the shack," or EMI within the house. I have one antenna setup of that form and whenever I use it, the RF resets the kitchen FM radio, causing it to lose track of time and memory. Most find it a better solution to have the antenna system stop somewhere outside the house and have a transmission line interconnect the radio and antenna.

With a remote tuner, the matching can be at or near the antenna, resulting in a well matched transmission line coming back to the radio. With the tuner at the radio, the matching takes place near the radio, and the SWR on the line out to the antenna will often be high. Note that in both cases the radio will be provided a good match and will happily put full power into the system. With the remote tuner, often more of the power will be radiated by the antenna and less will be dissipated as heat by the transmission line.

Some radios now come with automatic tuners as part of the radio. These can be functionally equivalent to the local tuner. The separate tuner does offer two advantages over the

Figure 14-17 — Automatic tuners from LDG, MFJ and SGC — ready for test.

internal tuner — it can support multiple radios, and most can match a higher SWR than many of the internal tuners. The key factor in deciding between a local and a remote tuner then becomes how much of the transmitter power actually reaches the antenna system and how much will heat up the transmission line. This is a function of operating frequency, SWR and line length.

The place to start the analysis is with *The ARRL Antenna Book*.[1] Figure 23 in Chapter 24 provides the attenuation in 100 feet of *matched* transmission line for each of the common types. Table 14 in the same chapter provides the *additional* loss for the non-matched case as a function of SWR and matched loss. [The same data is in Chapter 7 of this book.] Using the two tables, you can determine the total loss of your transmission line.

If the loss is acceptable, you can tune at the transmitter end. If not, by tuning at the antenna end you can eliminate most of the additional loss due to mismatch.

An example might be helpful. A multiband antenna such as my G5RV might have a 5:1 SWR on parts of

[1]Notes appear on page 14-35.

10 meters. If we feed it with 150 feet of RG-58 cable we have a matched loss of about 3.5 dB and the 5:1 SWR adds about another 2 dB for a total of 5.5 dB loss or about 71% of our power heating up the line! By moving the tuner to the antenna end of the coax, we reduce that to 55%. Another option is to change the transmission line (my solution immediately after making that calculation!).

If we go with lower loss RG-8 instead, we have a matched loss of about 2 dB (1.3 dB per 100 ft) and the SWR adds about another 0.3 dB for a total of 2.3 dB, or a loss of about 41% of our power. With the tuner at the antenna, the total loss would be the 2 dB or 37%—not much of a difference. Note that I didn't consider the tuner losses here, under the assumption that they would be the same at either location. The numbers get much more grim as the SWR goes up, by the way.

Two notes of caution—first, if you measure the SWR at the shack end of the cable, it will appear better than it is, due to the cable loss; second, the matched loss from Figure 23 is the *best* matched loss for new and dry cable. The actual loss can only go up from there, especially if the cable came from some dark corner of your basement, or worse, from an un-

known source at a flea market.

Note that all of these tuners are designed for unbalanced (coax) cable between the tuner and the radio and, with the exceptions noted, unbalanced operation on the antenna side (coax or single wire antennas) as well. In order to use these tuners with a balanced load, it is best to decouple the ground side of the tuner from the transmission line. A coax choke can be used, or a balun (balanced to unbalanced transformer) can be employed. If you are using a balun, it is best to keep the line impedance within a SWR of about 4:1 (with respect to the usual 200 Ω impedance of a 4:1 balun) to avoid heating, loss and possible balun damage. A subsequent planned review will look at the special class of unbalanced to balanced tuners that sidestep this issue in an elegant way and are once again appearing on the market.

A word or two about the data shown may be in order. Please note that we used the same precision resistive load set for each tuner. In most cases, this includes data outside the manufacturers' specification range. We measured at a single frequency in each band, and for 6 meters we just measured the case with a 1:1 load for all the tuners that claimed operation there.

LDG RT-11 and Z-100

A look at LDG's Web page, **www.ldgelectronics.com**, will show you their selection of tuners and accessories. In addition to the RT-11 remote control tuner and the Z-100 local tuner, tested (see **Figure 14-18**), they offer an autotuner rated at 1000 W. As this review was being prepared in 2004, they also announced a much more feature rich desktop unit to complement the very basic, but lower cost Z-100.

Figure 14-18 — LDG RT-11 (left) with control box and Z-100. A 12 ounce beverage container provides scale.

LDG RT-11

The RT-11 is a rugged, weatherproof tuner designed to be used inside or outdoors. It has coax connectors on input and output and is rated at 125 W from 1.8 to 30 and 50 W to 54 MHz. It is rated to match antennas with an SWR of 10:1 to 30 MHz and 3:1 from 50 to 54 MHz. This unit has an optional remote control designed to be used up to 100 feet from the tuner (15 foot cable supplied).

The remote control provides the ability to force a new tune, set for semi or full auto operation, keep the unit from tuning and allows bypassing of the tuner (straight through operation for matched antennas or out of band receive). In addition, LED indicators let you know the status and whether the SWR is below 1.5:1. One caution with the remote, the mounting bracket screws are not captive so you may want to use double-sided tape to secure it to a surface.

The RT-11 also has a jack to allow interfacing to radios designed to control proprietary tuners by emulating their commands. Special cables are offered to hook to various Alinco, ICOM, Kenwood and Yaesu radios for this purpose.

In my trials at home, I found that the RT-11 effortlessly tuned every antenna I had on all bands with a very low SWR, always well below 1.5:1. The tuning seemed to take about 5 seconds and hit the result the first time.

While automatic operation is possible without radio interface or remote control, I would have trouble imagining it and would suggest the remote for those without a compatible radio. For one thing, once tuned, it won't automatically restart the tuning process until the SWR reaches 3:1, a value that might cause many radios to "fold back" (reduce power) significantly.

The manual mentions that tuning should take place at the 25 W level, with full power applied only after tune is achieved, so that relay life will not be reduced. They also indicate that if a radio has the common power output fold back with high SWR it will automatically reduce power appropriately. I wouldn't count on that providing sufficient reduction, especially as the match is approached; I would instead manually reduce power while tuning.

LDG Z-100

The Z-100 is a self contained desk top unit with a 125 W rating (50 W on 6 meters). This unit is the first of a new series of tuners being released by LDG, with others providing additional features and controls. This is a basic unit corresponding to its low price, but none the less provides the needed tuning functions with straightforward "one button" operation. It includes memory of the settings for the last 200 matches made and tries those before it branches to its *unknown tune* algorithm. This is a clever idea that avoids the need to measure frequency. It is particularly useful for the case in which more than one antenna is used, since it really doesn't care — if it made the match before it will do it again, in a fraction of a second.

A feature of this unit is that it only draws power when actually tuning. Upon completion, the relays remain latched without power required until

---

Table 14-7

LDG RT-11 Remote Automatic Antenna Tuner

Manufacturer's Specifications
Input SWR range: to 10:1 (3:1 on 6 meters).
Output SWR range: not specified.
Frequency coverage: 1.8 to 54 MHz.
Input power: 0.1 to 125 W, 50 W on 6 meters.
Power requirements: 11 to 14 V dc, 7 to 250 mA.

Measured in ARRL Lab
See below.
See below.
As specified.
Tested at 50 W on HF, 20 W on 6 meters.
Idle 0 mA, max 140 mA at 13.8 V dc.

Measured power loss into resistive loads (%) / Input SWR at match:

SWR	Load (Ω)	160 Meters	80 Meters	40 Meters	20 Meters	10 Meters	6 Meters
16:1	3.125	No Match	No Match	27	22	<10	
				<1.5:1	2.6:1	<1.5:1	
8:1	6.25	No Match	17	17	19	20	
			<1.5:1	<1.5:1	<1.5:1	<1.5:1	
4:1	12.5	11	11	12	13	26	
		<1.5:1	<1.5:1	<1.5:1	<1.5:1	<2:1	
2:1	25	<10	<10	<10	<10	23	
		<1.5:1	<1.5:1	<1.5:1	<1.5:1	2.1:1	
1:1	50	<10	<10	<10	<10	<10	21
		<1.5:1	<1.5:1	<1.5:1	<1.5:1	<1.5:1	2.1:1
2:1	100	<10	<10	<10	<10	17	
		<2:1	<1.5:1	<1.5:1	<1.5:1	<1.5:1	
4:1	200	<10	<10	<10	<10	15	
		<2:1	<1.5:1	<1.5:1	<1.5:1	<1.5:1	
8:1	400	<10	<10	<10	<10	28	
		<1.5:1	<1.5:1	<1.5:1	<1.5:1	<1.5:1	
16:1	800	<10	12	<10	<10	19	
		<1.5:1	<1.5:1	<1.5:1	<1.5:1	<1.5:1	

Table 14-8
LDG Z-100 Desktop Automatic Antenna Tuner

Manufacturer's Specifications
Input SWR range: to 10:1 (3:1 on 6 meters).
Output SWR range: not specified.
Frequency coverage: 1.8 to 54 MHz.
Input power: 0.1 to 125 W, 50 W on 6 meters.
Power requirements: 7 to 18 V dc, 250 mA.

Measured in ARRL Lab
See below.
See below.
See text.
Tested at 50 W on HF, 20 W on 6 meters.
Idle 0 mA, max 160 mA at 13.8 V dc.

Measured power loss into resistive loads (%) / Input SWR at match:

SWR	Load (Ω)	160 Meters	80 Meters	40 Meters	20 Meters	10 Meters	6 Meters
16:1	3.125	No Match	No Match	15	10	<10	
				<1.5:1	<1.5:1	<1.5:1	
8:1	6.25	No Match	13	15	15	20	
			2.6:1	<2:1	<1.5:1	<2:1	
4:1	12.5	No Match	<10	<10	<10	<10	
			<1.5:1	<1.5:1	<2:1	<1.5:1	
2:1	25	<10	<10	<10	<10	17	
		<1.5:1	<1.5:1	<1.5:1	<1.5:1	<1.5:1	
1:1	50	<10	<10	<10	<10	<10	20
		<1.5:1	<1.5:1	<1.5:1	<1.5:1	<1.5:1	<2:1
2:1	100	<10	<10	<10	<10	<10	
		<1.5:1	<1.5:1	<1.5:1	<1.5:1	<1.5:1	
4:1	200	<10	<10	<10	11	<10	
		2.1:1	2.2:1	<1.5:1	<1.5:1	<1.5:1	
8:1	400	<10	<10	<10	11	<10	
		<1.5:1	<1.5:1	<1.5:1	<1.5:1	<2:1	
16:1	800	11	14	15	33	43	
		2.2:1	2.3:1	<1.5:1	<1.5:1	<1.5:1	

the next tune is requested. This is particularly appealing for portable low power operations in which every milliamp-hour is carried in.

The operation of this tuner is fundamentally different from the others in that it will only tune when the TUNE button is pushed. This has an advantage in that it will not start tuning inadvertently on high SWR, potentially applying full power during tune. Upon changing frequency, the operator can decide whether or not to initiate the tune cycle. By pushing the button for less than 0.5 seconds, the tuner goes to bypass. Between 0.5 and 3 seconds the tuner will attempt to find a match from memory (typically less than half a second), and only initiate a full tune if needed. If the button is pushed for more than 3 seconds a full tune cycle is initiated, ignoring any memorized settings.

This is easier to deal with than it sounds since the LEDs provide a confirmation of tuning mode. A green LED also indicates if the match is less than 1.5:1 or between 1.5 and 2:1. An early production unit exhibited some inconsistent tuning results on 6 meters. The manufacturer has developed a method of improved internal decoupling that solved this problem and the results reflect that change. LDG states that this will be included in future production units and that anyone having problems with 6 meter tuning on early units should contact them directly.

Manufacturer: LDG Electronics Inc, 1445 Parran Rd, PO Box 48, St Leonard, MD 20685; tel 877-890-3003; fax 410-586-8475; **www. ldgelectronics.com**. 2004 prices: RT-11 Tuner, $209; Remote head, $39; Z-100, $149; 12 V power cube for either tuner, $10.

MFJ-991

MFJ has recently announced a series of autotuners. All are in the typical indoor/ colocated configuration, but with the available remote kit (ordered, but not received in time for the review) can be used as a remote tuner if kept out of the weather. They offer the MFJ-991 (tested, as shown in **Figure 14-19**) 150 W rated tuner, a tuner with similar features rated at 600 W and a 300 W autotuner with digital display, balun and two port antenna switch. As with the LDG, the MFJ tuners require their tuning be accomplished at reduced power.

The MFJ-991 front panel provides full control capability and forward and reflected power metering with "crossed-needle" SWR measurement display. Two features of the '991 are not found on other tested units and are worth mentioning. First, the '991 has the capability to allow manually adjusting the C and L values of the tuner while in receive. This is helpful if you are using your radio for receive only and wish to attempt to match in order to increase signal strength. The second feature is the ability to select the SWR threshold

Figure 14-19 — MFJ-991 Autotuner.

at either 1.5 or 2:1.

In our testing the tuner went to the best match it could find in either case. The difference was in how far you could change frequency before it would automatically retune when you transmitted. If your radio can tolerate a 2:1 SWR, this could provide a benefit. The '991 could tune my G5RV on all bands and remembered the last setting for each frequency (1000 memories), with a one-click reset. Tuning the first time on a frequency was typical of the cycle time of the other units. This unit sounded somewhat louder (it has 18 heavy duty relays) than the other test samples, although not an issue for the single click associated with a memorized tune.

The MFJ-991 can interoperate with ICOM and Alinco tuner control commands. Appropriate interface cables are available from MFJ.

In addition to the obvious controls and indicators, there are some subtle ones as well. There are a number of meter "signals" sent to the operator that will not be clear without a cruise through the manual. For example, if you forget to reduce power before tuning, the power meter swings to full scale and the tuner is bypassed. If you toggle between 1.5 and 2:1 SWR threshold, the meter briefly jumps up to indicate that SWR.

Manufacturer: To order, or for your nearest MFJ dealer, call MFJ Enterprises at 800-647-1800 or order at **www.mfjenterprises. com**, fax 662-323-6551; or write MFJ Enterprises, Inc, 300 Industrial Park Rd, Starkville, MS 39759. [2004] Price: $220.

Table 14-9
MFJ-991 Desktop/Remote Automatic Antenna Tuner

Manufacturer's Specifications	*Measured in ARRL Lab*
Input Impedance range: 6 to 3200 Ω.	See below.
Output SWR range: 1.5:1 or 2:1 selectable.	See below.
Frequency coverage: 1.8 to 30 MHz.	As specified.
Input power: 5 to 150 W.	Tested at 50 W.
Power requirements: 12 to 15 V dc, 1.0 A.	Idle 90-300 mA, max 500 mA at 13.8 V dc.

Measured power loss into resistive loads (%) / Input SWR at match:

SWR	Load (Ω)	160 Meters	80 Meters	40 Meters	20 Meters	10 Meters
16:1	3.125	No Match	27	20	15	<10
			<1.5:1	<1.5:1	<1.5:1	<2:1
8:1	6.25	12	14	15	24	19
		<1.5:1	<1.5:1	<1.5:1	<1.5:1	2.6:1
4:1	12.5	<10	<10	<10	<10	12
		<1.5:1	<1.5:1	<1.5:1	<1.5:1	<1.5:1
2:1	25	<10	<10	<10	<10	<10
		<1.5:1	<1.5:1	<1.5:1	<1.5:1	<1.5:1
1:1	50	<10	<10	<10	<10	<10
		<1.5:1	<1.5:1	<1.5:1	<1.5:1	<1.5:1
2:1	100	<10	<10	<10	<10	<10
		<1.5:1	<1.5:1	<1.5:1	<1.5:1	<1.5:1
4:1	200	<10	<10	<10	<10	<10
		<1.5:1	<1.5:1	<1.5:1	<1.5:1	<1.5:1
8:1	400	<10	<10	<10	11	11
		<1.5:1	<1.5:1	<1.5:1	<1.5:1	<1.5:1
16:1	800	<10	16	<10	<10	23
		<1.5:1	<1.5:1	<1.5:1	<1.5:1	<1.5:1

SGC SG-237 and MAC-200

SGC has been making automatic antenna tuners for many years, and offers a wide selection. Until recently, they concentrated on remote tuners, usually the weatherproof type, at power ratings of 100 to 500 W. More recently, they have introduced a number of variations of their SG-237, a board version to build into your own radio or antenna cabinet, an open enclosure model for remote but indoor use and one with controls and indicators intended for portable use. They have recently released a Multiple Antenna Controller, MAC-200. The units we tested were an SG-237 (one that has fed the backstay of my sailboat for some years) and a relatively new combination unit, the MAC-200 (as shown in **Figure 14-20**).

SGC SG-237 Autotuner

The SG-237 was the first in a series of SGC tuners that were much more compact than their previous (and continuing) line, the SG-230 (200 W, 1.6-30 MHz), SG-231 (100 W, 1-60 MHz) and SG-235 (500 W,

Figure 14-20 — SGC SG-237 (left) and MAC-200.

1.8-30 MHz). The SG-237 is rated at 100 W PEP, both for operation and for tuning (40 W continuous carrier power). The transmitter connection is via a 9 foot combined RF, control and power cable (25 and 50 foot extensions are available), while the antenna connection is via a single ceramic insulated terminal. While the tuner is designed to feed a single wire against ground, I have successfully employed mine into coax fed antennas as well as loops and single wires.

This is a rugged unit in a compact waterproof aluminum enclosure that can slide in almost anywhere. It needs no remote control box to work, and I've used mine that way for years. An

optional remote control is offered (and we tested with it) to provide a positive indication of match and to allow a lockout or a forced reset. The lockout can be handy in a portable or mobile environment to avoid the tuner attempting to retune due to the temporary proximity of outside objects while in motion, for example.

The '237 provides a memory function that uses the measured transmitter frequency to result in the tuner settings last used to successfully tune to that frequency. This means that instead of taking 5 to 10 seconds to tune, the previously stored settings for a frequency are applied in milliseconds and used if the resulting SWR

Table 14-10

SGC SG-237 Remote Automatic Antenna Tuner

Manufacturer's Specifications
Input SWR range: corresponding to a
  minimum 7 foot antenna above 3.5 MHz,
  23 feet above 1.8 MHz.
Output SWR range: 1.4:1 typical.
Frequency coverage: 1.8 to 60 MHz.
Input power: 3 to 100 W.
Power requirements: 10.5 to 18 V dc, 300 mA. Idle and tuning 270 to 480 mA at 13.8 V dc.

Measured in ARRL Lab
See below.

See below.
As specified.
Tested at 50 W.

Measured power loss into resistive loads (%) / Input SWR at match:

SWR	Load (Ω)	160 Meters	80 Meters	40 Meters	20 Meters	10 Meters	6 Meters
16:1	3.125	21	21	19	No Match	<10	
		<1.5:1	<1.5:1	<1.5:1		<1.5:1	
8:1	6.25	16	18	20	24	23	
		<1.5:1	2.1:1	<1.5:1	<1.5:1	<1.5:1	
4:1	12.5	11	12	15	17	23	
		<1.5:1	<1.5:1	<1.5:1	<1.5:1	<1.5:1	
2:1	25	<10	11	21	18	26	
		<1.5:1	<1.5:1	<2:1	<2:1	<1.5:1	
1:1	50	<10	<10	<10	<10	12	29
		<1.5:1	<1.5:1	<1.5:1	<1.5:1	<1.5:1	<1.5:1
2:1	100	<10	<10	<10	13	14	
		<2:1	<2:1	<1.5:1	<1.5:1	<1.5:1	
4:1	200	No Match	<10	<10	16	10	
			2.1:1	<1.5:1	<1.5:1	<1.5:1	
8:1	400	No Match	<10	10	16	18	
			2.1:1	<1.5:1	<1.5:1	<1.5:1	
16:1	800	<10	<10	14	30	58	
		<1.5:1	<1.5:1	<1.5:1	<1.5:1	<2:1	

is less than 2:1. In some cases they won't be right (and a new tune will be initiated), if a different antenna is used, for example, but their concept is that this tuner is out where the antenna is and thus should see the same impedance for a given frequency each time that frequency is employed.

SGC MAC-200 Multiple Antenna Controller

This device combines a 200 W autotuner, a five port automatic or manual antenna switch, power and SWR meters and a balun in one compact package. This is a nice unit and quickly grew on me in operation. It has enough controls and indicators to keep me entertained even when the bands aren't open.

For some time, most manual tuners have had provisions for switching antennas as well as tuning them. This is very handy, since even those with just one antenna should have a dummy load to switch to for tune up. I have no numbers, but I would guess more hams have more than one HF antenna than have only one. I don't have fancy HF antennas, but I have a G5RV I use on 80 through 10, a Lazy-H, perpendicular to the G5RV for 30 through 10 meters and a 70 foot wire vertical for use when it makes sense (not often in my part of New England).

With the MAC-200, I can memorize which antenna to use on which band. It switches antennas on the first dot of a CW string (full power—no problem) and I'm there. As noted, at my station, on some bands the antenna is a function of the direction to the distant station, I can just touch the MANUAL button and I can select a different antenna by touching a button numbered 1 to 5.

As configured, antenna one is intended for balanced feed, antenna two has a terminal for a single wire feed, and three through five are terminated in UHF (SO-239) coax connector jacks.

The separate meters for power and SWR are handy. The SWR meter is especially convenient in that it computes and indicates SWR independent of power level without an adjustment. The manual warns that the meters are not of the precision type and I can attest to that. Their meter indicated 80 W while my Bird 43 showed 100. This is still very useful to let you know if all is well.

This is a handy unit, in a cabinet matching the cross section of the SGC-2020 transceiver (but somewhat longer), it can be made to fit in most shacks. In mine it can slide beneath the shelf that holds my equipment three inches above the desk, for example.

The one limitation some may have is it provides a "typical" match of 2:1. Well 2:1 is fine for some transmitters, while others may start to "fold back" above 1.5:1 and this may be a problem if yours is in that group. On the other hand, looking at the data it is clear that most of the time it was below 1.5:1 with our loads.

Our original unit remembered which antenna to use on each band, but didn't memorize tuner settings. A warranty replacement unit had a flawless memory function.

Manufacturer: SGC Inc, 13737 SE 26th St, Bellevue, WA 98005; tel 425-746-6310; fax 425-746-6384; **www.sgcworld.com**. 2004 price: SG-237, $360; Smartlock remote control, $59; MAC-200, $360.

Table 14-11

SGC MAC-200 Desktop Automatic Antenna Tuner and Controller

Manufacturer's Specifications	Measured in ARRL Lab
Input impedance range: 5-1000 (feed line) 0.2-5000 (long wire).	See below.
Output SWR range: 2:1 typical.	See below.
Frequency coverage: 1.8 to 60 MHz.	As specified.
Input power: 1.5 to 200 W.	Tested at 50 W.
Power requirements: 10 to 18.5 V dc, 230 mA. Idle 240 mA, max 490 mA at 13.8 V dc (meter light off)	Idle 280 mA, max 530 mA at 13.8 V dc (meter light on)

Measured power loss into resistive loads (%) / Input SWR at match:

SWR	Load (Ω)	160 Meters	80 Meters	40 Meters	20 Meters	10 Meters	6 Meters
16:1	3.125	No Match	39	24	<10	<10	
			<2:1	<2:1	<1.5:1	<1.5:1	
8:1	6.25	No Match	16	18	15	30	
			<1.5:1	<1.5:1	<1.5:1	<1.5:1	
4:1	12.5	<10	<10	<10	18	27	
		<1.5:1	<1.5:1	<1.5:1	<1.5:1	<1.5:1	
2:1	25	<10	<10	<10	<10	25	
		<1.5:1	<1.5:1	<1.5:1	<1.5:1	2:1	
1:1	50	<10	<10	<10	<10	12	27
		<2:1	<1.5:1	<1.5:1	<1.5:1	<2:1	<2:1
2:1	100	<10	<10	<10	<10	14	
		<1.5:1	<2:1	<2:1	<2:1	<1.5:1	
4:1	200	<10	<10	<10	<10	14	
		<1.5:1	<1.5:1	<1.5:1	<1.5:1	<2:1	
8:1	400	<10	<10	13	15	17	
		<1.5:1	<1.5:1	<1.5:1	<1.5:1	<1.5:1	
16:1	800	No Match	22	14	25	31	
			<1.5:1	<1.5:1	<1.5:1	<1.5:1	

Medium to High Power Auto Antenna Tuners — The Evolution Continues

Reviewed by Joel R. Hallas, W1ZR
QST *Technical Editor,*
QST *August 2006*

We last looked at a selection of automatic antenna tuners in May 2004 (see previous section). At that time, we picked four examples, two designed for remote operation and two desktop units. While different in many ways, they all were limited to 100 to 200 W. Higher powered automatic antenna tuners have been available, but they were either built into high powered amplifiers (ICOM or Yaesu, for example), were designed for remote operation as in the SGC SG-235, or have been discontinued, as in the case of the Ten-Tec 253.[2]

High powered automatic antenna tuners initially appeared in the 1980s — the Heath 2500, J.W. Miller AT2500, and Daiwa CNA-1001 — but they were not as sophisticated as the units reviewed here, requiring some manual adjustment or presetting of the inductor for best operation.[3,4,5]

Modern solid state transceivers and linear amplifiers with their "no tune" output stages have been well received, especially by those of us who grew up in the vacuum tube era.

The typical transmitter of that time required careful adjustment of the transmitter TUNE, LOAD and DRIVE controls, at a minimum, every time we changed frequency. Failure to do it right could result in destruction of the final amplifier tubes — sometimes a pricey proposition. The other side of the coin is that those transmitters could be adjusted to match antenna loads with a much higher SWR than the current crop of radio gear.

The modern no-tune feature generally means "no tune if the SWR is 1.5:1 or less," something that often doesn't fit with real world antennas and wide amateur bands. The answer has been an antenna system matching unit, often called an antenna tuner, even though many would argue that it doesn't really tune the antenna — rather it transforms the impedance at the bottom of an antenna system to the 50 Ω the radio equipment wants to operate into. Setting semantics aside, it seems that the controls we used to have to adjust haven't disappeared but have moved from the radio to another box — the antenna tuner.

Enter the Automatic Antenna Tuner

To extend the no-tune concept all the way to the antenna requires a no-tune, or *automatic*, antenna tuner. As noted, these have been generally available for some time at the power levels of modern transceivers, Each of these tuners can effectively add an automatic antenna matching system to your medium to high power HF station, at least up to their power limits. Honor the caveats and you will appreciate the freedom they provide.

For this review we have selected three desktop models that span the medium to high power range and highlight some other differences as well. While they all fill the same spot in a station block diagram, they are quite different in several respects and thus should not be directly compared on a 1:1 basis. Rather, determine if one or more will meet your needs, desires and budget.

All of the tuners reviewed in the 2004 report shared the same adjustment mechanism — fixed inductors and capacitors switched by relays. The LDG and MFJ tuners reviewed here share that architecture as well, but with beefier components designed to meet the higher power requirements of their ratings. The Palstar AT-Auto is of a completely different design, a T network with a differential variable capacitor, half on each side of a shunting rotary inductor. The Palstar makes its adjustments via stepper motors rather than relays. Interestingly, while standalone tuners have tended to be of the relay type, many internal tuners have used motor driven capacitors. Motor driven components were also used in the high powered automatic tuners from the 1980s mentioned previously, so this is a time-tested approach. We'll look at each tuner in alphabetical order. These tuners from LDG, MFJ and Palstar offer the convenience of automatic tuning at medium to high power levels.

Figure 14-21 — Medium power tuners from Palstar, LDG and MFJ.

LDG AT-1000 Automatic Memory Antenna Tuner

The LDG AT-1000 sits squarely in the middle of the pack, both in terms of price and power rating. The 1000 W level fits nicely with a good selection of popular, not quite legal limit, linear amplifiers, including a couple announced at Dayton in 2006. All of the tuners reviewed here cover 160 through 10 meters, but the AT-1000 offers operation on 6 meters at the 100 W level as well.

The LDG, in common with the other units, has memories to allow a rapid return to the last previously matched settings. In the case of the AT-1000, there are 200 memory locations and the tuner will reset to them in less than half a second. If the antenna you are tuning does not have a memorized setting that works, the tuner can spend up to 8 seconds finding a match, but will remember for the next time.

The LDG approach to memory management is different from some. Some others tuners store settings based on frequency. This is a great approach if you will be tuning a single antenna for each band. In the LDG AT-1000, the last 200 successful matches are stored independent of frequency. A new match request quickly cycles through the 200 to see if a match is found before it begins its tune algorithm. This is a particularly beneficial approach if you switch the tuner output to different antennas on the same band, since it doesn't have to relearn parameters for a particular frequency every time you change antennas. It also avoids the need for frequency measuring circuitry within the tuner.

The AT-1000 has a fairly Spartan front panel that doesn't immediately show its capabilities. LDG has made

Table 14-12
LDG AT-1000

Manufacturer's Specifications

Maximum power, 1000 W SSB, 750 W CW, 500 W digital, 100 W 6 meters. 20 W while tuning (100 W with foldback), 75 W (3:1 SWR), 125 W (1:1 SWR).
Minimum power for tuning: 5 W.
Frequency range: 1.8 to 54 MHz.

Tuning time: 1 to 8 seconds. 0.5 second if memorized
Input impedance: 6 to 800 ..
Power required: 11 to 15 V, 1 A.
Dimensions (height, width, depth): 3 × 13 × 9 inches.
Weight: 6 pounds.

Measured power loss into resistive loads (%) / Input SWR at match. Tested at 50 W.

SWR	Load (Ω)	160 m	80 m	40 m	20 m	10 m
16:1	3.125	No match n/a	No match n/a	No match n/a	No match n/a	No match n/a
8:1	6.25	No match n/a	No match n/a	* **	20 1.6:1	22 **
4:1	12.5	12 2.3:1	* **	* **	* **	18 2.2:1
2:1	25	* **	* **	* **	* **	* **
1:1	50	* **	* **	* **	* **	* **
2:1	100	* **	* **	* **	* 2.1:1	* **
4:1	200	* **	* **	* **	* **	* **
8:1	400	16 2.1:1	* **	* **	22 2.1:1	17 **
16:1	800	No match n/a	18 **	17 **	55 **	No match n/a

*Power loss less than or equal to 10%.
**Matched SWR less than or equal to 1.5:1.

Figure 14-23 — Rear panel connections on the LDG AT-1000.

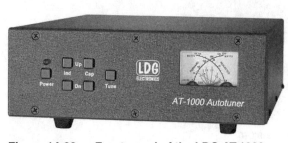

Figure 14-22 — Front panel of the LDG AT-1000.

Figure 14-24 — Interior circuitry of the LDG AT-1000.

maximum use of the cross needle wattmeter on the front panel, going further with information delivery than I would have imagined with such a straightforward display. The cross needle wattmeter has two scales, reading forward (1000 W) and reflected (180 W) power simultaneously. The point at which the meter pointers cross is a third scale directly reading in SWR. So far it's just like every other cross needle meter we've seen.

What sets the AT-1000 apart is that LDG has additional indicator functionality that appears as a set of semaphore signals between tuner and operator. Each needle is driven independently in this mode and each can vary in speed and position as it fills you in on the tuner's condition and status. For example, if during a tuning cycle, both arms quickly raise fully (in surrender?) it means too much power has been supplied to allow it to safely tune. It then switches to bypass mode and goes on break until you reduce power and restart the tuning cycle.

Another feature is the ability to change the inductance and capacitance parameters manually. This can be a benefit in at least two ways. First it allows manual fine trimming of the tuning in case you want a better SWR than the tuner finds automatically. Manual tuning can also be used to peak up the receive signal strength if you're listening to a station on a frequency that you can't transmit on. This could include shortwave broadcast frequencies or bands or segments for which you don't yet have license privileges.

How'd it Work? At my station the AT-1000 did everything I asked of it without problems. My antennas tuned satisfactorily on all bands. Memorized settings were recalled without difficulty in a fraction of a second. The 15 page multicolor manual does a good job of describing how to set up and use the tuner. A table of "meter bounce codes" is included, and you will likely want to keep a copy at hand, unless your memory is much better than mine. ARRL Lab test results are shown in **Table 14-12**.

Manufacturer: LDG Electronics, 1445 Parran Rd, St Leonard, MD 20685; tel 410-586-8475; **ldg@ldgelectronics.com**; **www. ldgelectronics.com**. 2006 price: $599.

MFJ-994 Intellituner Automatic Antenna Tuner

At first glance, the MFJ-994 appears to be a very similar tuner to the AT-1000. It has almost the same controls and indicators as the LDG tuner, although they are on opposite sides of the front panel. It makes use of a similar set of semaphore indications. The major differences are:

• The MFJ tuner has a lower maximum power rating (600 vs 1000 W PEP and 300 vs 750 W CW) and a correspondingly lower price.

• The '994 provides an interface to allow operation using the TUNE button on Alinco, ICOM, Kenwood or Yaesu radios equipped to control an antenna tuner. An accessory cable is required to activate this function.

• The '994 has more memory locations, all indexed by frequency.

• The '994 offers a choice of two power meter scales, 3000 or 300 W forward power with corresponding 600 or 60 W reflected power at full scale.

During the review process, we determined that the MFJ-994 has now been superseded by the MFJ-994B. The functionality and operation are similar, with the same tuning and switching elements. The main difference seems to be the memory management function, with the B

Figure 14-26 — Rear panel connections on the MFJ-994.

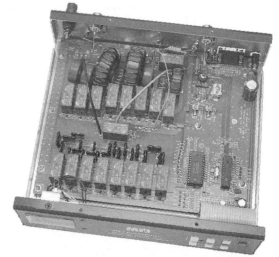

Figure 14-27 — Interior circuitry of the MFJ-994.

Figure 14-25 — Front panel of the MFJ-994.

Table 14-13
MFJ-994

Manufacturer's Specifications

Maximum power, 600 W PEP SSB, 300 W CW, 20 W while tuning (100 W with foldback).
Minimum power for tuning: 10 W.
Frequency range: 1.8 to 30 MHz.

Input impedance: 12 to 800.
Power required: 12 to 15 V, 1 A.
Dimensions (height, width, depth) 2.8 × 10.1 × 9.2 inches.
Weight: 3.7 pounds.

Measured power loss into resistive loads (%) / Input SWR at match. Tested at 50 W.

SWR	Load (Ω)	160 m	80 m	40 m	20 m	10 m
16:1	3.125	No Match	No Match	10	12	*
		n/a	n/a	2.6:1	2.2:1	2.0:1
8:1	6.25	13	13	*	13	15
		2.4:1	1.8:1	**	**	2.2:1
4:1	12.5	*	*	*	*	15
		**	**	**	**	1.8:1
2:1	25	*	*	*	*	*
		**	**	**	**	**
1:1	50	*	*	*	*	*
		**	**	**	**	**
2:1	100	*	*	*	*	*
		**	**	**	**	**
4:1	200	*	*	*	*	*
		**	**	**	**	**
8:1	400	*	*	*	14	*
		**	**	**	**	1.8:1
16:1	800	*	17	16	11	*
		**	**	**	1.8:1	1.7:1

*Power loss less than or equal to 10%.
**Matched SWR less than or equal to 1.5:1.

model including a virtual memory function said to store up to 10,000 frequency data points versus 1000 in the earlier '994. The other difference noted in the specs is that the new one can tune with a minimum of 2 W, versus 10 W in the original.

The MFJ has some control flexibility hidden behind its few buttons. The "tuned" threshold can be set to either 1.5:1 or 2:1. With the 1.5:1 setting, the match is closer, but it will take a bit longer to find. While 2:1 should happen more quickly, some radios won't put out full power into a 2:1 load. It's nice to have the choice. An "auto tune" function is also provided that causes the tuner to activate if the SWR goes above your threshold by a user selectable 0.5, 1.0 or 1.5. This is handy as you change frequency, but be careful it doesn't drop into tuning mode while you are at full power. Pushing in the AUTO button unambiguously disables the auto tune function, entirely avoiding this concern.

In Summary The MFJ-994 did everything just as promised. It showed no problem handling the 600 W we could deliver, the only tuner of the group that we could test to the limit! It was too quick for me to stopwatch the tuning speed, but my sense was, as expected, that the frequency based memories were a bit quicker if all operations were using the same antenna. It also appeared that the MFJ relays were a bit quieter than the other relay operated tuner, but that could have been because there were generally fewer cycles needed before it was matched. ARRL Lab test results are shown in **Table 14-13**.

MFJ provided a comprehensive 23 page, well illustrated, instruction manual that was clear in its description of how the unit operated and what to expect of it.

Manufacturer: MFJ Enterprises, 300 Industrial Park Rd, Starkville, MS 39759; tel 662-323-5869, fax 662-323-6551; **www. mfjenterprises. com**. 2006 price: $359.95. Auto tuner radio interface cables: MFJ-5124A for Alinco, $19.95 MFJ-5124I for ICOM, $19.95 MFJ-5124K for Kenwood, $59.95; MFJ-5124Y for Yaesu, $59.95.

PALSTAR AT-AUTO

As noted previously, the AT-Auto is of a different architecture than the other tuners in this review. Palstar is noted for its line of high quality manual antenna tuners, so it should not be a surprise that Palstar decided to build its first auto tuner using the same type of in-house constructed parts that have been successful in their other offerings.

This is a large and complex device with features that I haven't seen before in any tuner. The first feature you might notice is the cross needle wattmeter that takes up the left side of the front panel. This is the same display and circuitry built into their PM2000A standalone wattmeter. It provides both average and peak forward and reflected power readings at full scale power levels of 3000/600 (forward/reflected) and 300/60 W. This is an upgrade to the Palstar WM150 wattmeter reviewed in July 2002 with the addition of a PEAK HOLD setting with a 2 second hold time.

The right side of the panel includes a two-line liquid crystal display (LCD), a knob for manual tuning (more later), MANUAL/AUTO and SELECT buttons. It is on this side of the panel that interesting things happen. As with most auto tuners, you apply power and it starts to match your antenna to 50 Ω. What's different with the AT-Auto's tuning sequence is that it first measures frequency, tells you the operating frequency and then politely asks you to turn off your transmitter while it finds a close match. It has a default set of L and C values for each frequency and runs its quiet motors until they are in range. It then asks for

another dose of RF to refine the tune. Every time it does this, like a good smart machine, it memorizes its settings and uses them the next time you use that frequency. This approach minimizes interference to others.

A well thought out and, to my knowledge, unique feature of this tuner is its use of a radio interface. This, and many other auto tuners, make use of a radio's tuner interface to initiate the tuning sequence and cause a reduced-power tune signal to be sent from the radio. The AT-Auto has an additional connection from the radio's CAT (computer interface) port. The CAT port provides frequency data from the radio to the tuner. As you tune the receiver, the tuner indicates the frequency and follows along with either its default or memorized values. This means that, if you've been on that frequency before, the tuner will be tuned before you hit the key or PTT! If you haven't been there before, it will use its default values and still be pretty close.

This is particularly handy if you are listening to a frequency at which you aren't licensed to transmit, for example WWV or shortwave broad-

cast frequencies. The cable for ICOM radios is provided. You do have to think a bit while you use it (yes we have to be even smarter than our smart devices!). The CAT frequency data reflects the frequency of whichever VFO is active. If you are operating split frequency, it will tune back and forth between the two VFO frequencies as you switch between them. This is not likely much of an issue if you are operating in the typical "up five" (VFOs just 5 kHz apart) environment, but could be a disaster if you are operating cross-band split for some reason. The solution — while you have the VFO on your transmit frequency and the tuner properly tuned, tap the MANUAL/AUTO button so that it will be in manual mode and the automation will take a break.

The CAT function, as we wrote this, is available only for radios that support ICOM's CI-V protocol. Palstar expects to have cables and software upgrades to allow interoperation with Kenwood and Yaesu radios soon. Speaking of software, Palstar kindly provides a 9-pin serial cable designed to allow you to install

Figure 14-29 — Rear panel connections on the Palstar AT-Auto.

Figure 14-28 — Front panel of the Palstar AT-Auto.

Figure 14-30 — Interior circuitry of the Palstar AT-Auto.

upgraded software when it is available. As we write this, there is no information on how to do this in either the manual or on the Palstar Web site. On the other hand, there is no new software either, so presumably when there's something new to download, they will tell us how to do it. We did successfully download upgraded software for their ZM-30 Antenna Analyzer during that review, so they seem to be able to deal with the process. We understand from Palstar that revised firmware to improve 10 meter operation has been developed and will be available shortly.

Another nice feature of the AT-Auto is that it has provisions for switch selection (via the front panel SELECT button) of either a balanced (through a 4:1 balun at the output) or an unbalanced (coax connected) antenna. The switch doesn't just insert the balun, but provides two completely independent antenna connections, so both can be always available. The memory associates the settings with each antenna port separately, so if you switch between antennas while on the same band, it thoughtfully remembers the settings for each.

New production tuners will also include BYPASS selection. A factory upgrade is said to be available for early production units. Want to do it Yourself? Poke the MANUAL/AUTO button and you are into manual tuning mode. The single knob below the LCD display is used to change the inductance or capacitance. It comes up ready to tune the C; push the knob in briefly and it changes the L. The value of L and C are displayed on the LCD panel as you change them, so you can record the values for later reference. It moves the adjustments via the stepper motors, so minimum effort is required — no heavy cranking needed.

So how'd it work? We really liked the concept of this tuner. By its nature it can provide finer adjustment than the relay types we have seen, although their resolution could be made arbitrarily fine with additional relays and smaller increments of C and L, and higher cost. We also liked the

quietness of the motors compared to the clacking relays. The downside can be tuning time. As noted above, with a CATconnected radio and memorized settings it rapidly follows you as you tune. A change in bands can take longer. We measured the following times to retune between bands:

From (Meters)	To	Tune Time (Seconds)
80	40	11
40	30	4
30	20	3
20	15	2
15	10	2
160	10	45

The times shown are between memorized settings. To tune from a default setting to a finely tuned condition takes about 2 additional seconds if there isn't already a memorized setting for the frequency. It seems especially quick with the CAT function, since it feels like it's all tuned and waiting for you to catch up!

The AT-Auto comes with a well illustrated 20 page manual. The manual assumes you know why you wanted an antenna tuner and where you are going to connect it. This wasn't much of a problem since it has such an informative display, although, if you're expecting "open left flap, remove tuner from box…" type instructions, this manual isn't quite up to that standard.

On the down side, we had just a few disappointments. Initially, the tuner wouldn't match my antenna on 12 and 10 meters. On 12 meters, my measured SWR was 6:1 at the tuner. While it couldn't find a perfect match, and announced MATCH NOT FOUND! on the LCD panel, it actually got to within a 2.4:1 SWR, which my radio found acceptable. On 10 meters my antenna showed an SWR of 3:1 and the best the tuner could do was 2.78:1. In both of these cases, the LCD panel noted that the inductance was at L=000.

This suggested to me that it was the particular value of complex impedance rather than the SWR that was causing the problem. I put in an additional 6 feet of 50 Ω coax to move "around the Smith Chart" and the tuner was then able to find a

perfect match in both cases. This is a good trick to keep in mind if faced with this kind of problem with any tuner. The indicator was very helpful in pointing me in the right direction.

A less significant problem was that the frequency metering system required more power to determine the frequency on the higher bands. On 160 through 15 meters, the 10 W that the ICOM transceiver put out in TUNE mode was plenty to allow the frequency to be read and the tune function to be initiated. On 12 and 10 meters, at 10 W, I received a FREQUENCY ERROR CHECK CARRIER LEVEL message on the LCD. It took more power to allow the frequency to be read. This was no problem with another transceiver that allows me to crank it up as far as I want when the TUNE button is pressed, but the ICOM had a fixed level. A quick fix is to switch to AM or FM mode to put out more power. Just hit the bar on your PTT microphone or use a straight key in CW mode.

Upon further investigation, I found that it worked fine on all bands with 10 W to a matched load. At some impedances, apparently there was not enough signal for the measuring circuits. Another workaround would be to manually set it within range and then let the AT-Auto fine tune to perfection. A handy feature of this tuner is that it can be tuned at 1500 W with no relay contacts to burn. This is good since it sometimes notices a bit of reflected power and trims the adjustment after you turn on the amplifier. ARRL Lab test results are shown in **Table 14-14**.

Manufacturer: Palstar Inc, 9676 N Looney Rd, Piqua, OH 45356; tel 800-773-7931, fax 937-773-8003; **info@palstar.com**; **www.palstar.com**. 2006 price: $1195.

In Summary

Each of these tuners did what they said they would over most of their frequency range and each could be of benefit to operators using higher power than that handled by other automatic antenna tuners. Some care needs to be taken with their operation, beyond that found in the lower

Table 14-14
Palstar AT-Auto

Manufacturer's Specifications

Maximum power: 1500 W single tone.
Frequency range: 1.8 to 30 MHz.
Input impedance: 160 to 20 meters, 1200
±j1200; 15 to 10 meters 1000 ±j1000.

Tuning time: 1-30 seconds.
Dimensions (height, width, depth):
  5.5 × 12.5 × 16 inches.
Weight: 25 pounds.

Measured power loss into resistive loads (%) / Input SWR at match. Tested at 50 W.

SWR	Load (Ω)	160 m	80 m	40 m	20 m	10 m
16:1	3.125	54 **	33 **	19 **	* **	No Match n/a
8:1	6.25	42 **	24 **	15 **	12 **	No Match n/a
4:1	12.5	30 **	17 **	14 **	* **	No Match n/a
2:1	25	24 **	12 **	* **	* **	26 **
1:1	50	16 **	* **	* **	* **	* **
2:1	100	13 **	* **	* **	* **	20 **
4:1	200	11 **	* **	* **	12 **	43 **
8:1	400	12 **	* **	11 **	23 **	42 **
16:1	800	16 1.6:1	25 **	24 **	55 **	49 **

*Power loss less than or equal to 10%.
**Matched SWR less than or equal to 1.5:1.

powered units, because of the power involved and particularly because of the difference between "tuning power" and "operating power." Each unit is specified to be tuned using reduced power from the exciter at somewhere in the 10 to 100 W range.

Each tuner finds a match at that power level and then it should be safe to switch on the linear amplifier — but is it? With the MFJ and Palstar tuners, there were conditions under which it would initiate the tuning cycle again at full power, even after being within specification at the lower tuning power. The reason is likely a combination of a larger sample of RF to make reflected power measurement and nonlinearity of the detectors, not surprising for analog circuitry. Different tuners will react differently under this circumstance. The Palstar actually doesn't mind tuning at 1500 W and will calmly trim up without a whimper. The MFJ tuner will note that it is tuning above the specified tuning power spec and switch to bypass — whoops, you had the linear pre-tuned with a dummy load so that it would be ready to go, and now it sees a 9:1 SWR, or whatever your antenna has, going directly to the amplifier. This could cause a catastrophic reaction in your amplifier! The LDG tuner is different in this regard. It only initiates a tune cycle if the TUNE button is pressed.

So what to do? There are two potential solutions. One, manually trim up the tuning for an even lower SWR using the L and C up and down buttons. If the reflected power is fully nulled, it should avoid this problem. The other approach is to switch the tuner to manual mode after it finds its initial match. That will prevent it from automatically retuning while high power is applied. Or do both. Arguably this changes tuner operation from "auto" to "semi-auto," but I recommend it for any high power relay switched tuner. The consequences of not doing so could be extreme to either the amplifier or the relay contacts or both.

A New Generation of Balanced Antenna Tuners

Reviewed by Joel R. Hallas, W1ZR
QST *Technical Editor*
QST *September 2004*

A new breed of antenna tuner available in different flavors from multiple manufacturers addresses concerns about using baluns with high SWR to feed balanced antenna systems. Paul Danzer's article in the April 2004 issue of *QST* brought to paper a concern many of us have had for some time — the use of baluns at the output of antenna tuners.[6] As noted in his article, if the balanced load is near the balun's design impedance (typically 200 Ω for the usual 4:1 balun) all is well.

Unfortunately, the typical random sized center fed antenna with random length ladder line feed has an impedance at the feed point that varies dramatically with frequency. The result can be heating and loss (and occasional damage) at the balun. These effects were well documented in a series of *QST* articles by Frank Witt and later in a performance evaluation of unbalanced tuners with both balanced and unbalanced loads.[7,8]

So How Do We Fix the Problem?

As Danzer noted, the classic solu-tion has been the use of an inherently balanced tuner. The commercially manufactured E.F. Johnson Matchbox tuners of the '50s worked reasonably well in their day, and over the bands that they covered (we didn't have the 60, 30, 17 and 12 meter bands back then). Now at least three manufactur-ers have begun offering balanced antenna tuners of a different configu-ration. For this review we selected the MFJ-974H and the Palstar AT1500BAL and AT4K. Interest-ingly, each of the three uses a different architecture, and each is different from the design of the old Matchbox!

In addition to those units, SGC has announced a low power self-con-tained auto-tuner, the SG-211, which shares the design concept of the AT4K and will be the subject of an upcoming Short Takes column. We thought it would be good to evaluate the performance of the medium and high-power units and provide a comparison to the old Johnson tuner.

What's in the New Tuners?

Glad you asked! As noted, each of the tuners uses a different design configuration. Each can be directly compared to some of the common unbalanced configurations. Note that the power ratings and price of the Palstar tuners put them in a different category from the MFJ units and thus, direct comparisons may not be appropriate. Both the MFJ and the Palstar AT1500BAL are fully balanced tuners — the MFJ a dual T section design with shunt L, and the Palstar a dual L section with shunt C. The Palstar AT4K tuner takes a completely different approach. It uses the insulated unbalanced scheme suggested in Paul's article and described in detail in *The ARRL Antenna Book*.[9]

The relationship of the designs to their more commonly encountered unbalanced configurations are shown in simplified schematics in **Figures 14-32** through **14-33**. The other differ-ences between the units are in their ratings. The MFJ tuner covers 160 through 6 meters, while the Palstar tuners top out at 10 meters. Both Palstar tuners are rated at 1500 W or greater (the AT4K has a reduced rating below a 25 Ω load) while the MFJ tuner is rated at 300 W PEP, 150 W CW.

The ratings of the Johnson Match-boxes were established in a day when amateur power levels were specified based on average dc power *input*, rather than the current PEP RF *output*

Figure 14-31 — From the top the MFJ-974H, the Palstar AT1500BAL and AT4K. On the right, they are being scrutinized by their logical ancestor, the Johnson Matchbox.

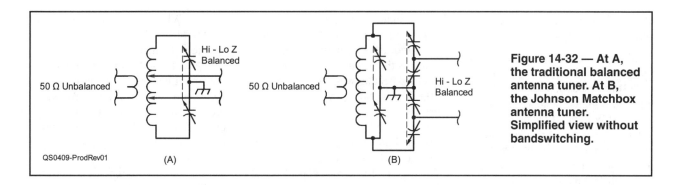

Figure 14-32 — At A, the traditional balanced antenna tuner. At B, the Johnson Matchbox antenna tuner. Simplified view without bandswitching.

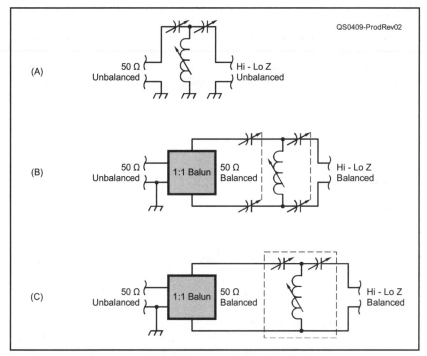

Figure 14-33 — At A, an unbalanced T-network tuner. At B, a balanced T-network tuner. At C, an unbalanced T-network tuner for balanced loads.

power. A "275 W" Johnson matchbox was thus rated to work with transmitters running 275 W dc input, or about 200 W average output. This was in the day of plate modulated AM service, so that rating further translates to 800 W PEP under today's rules. Similarly, a "kW Matchbox" would likely be rated today as a 3 kW PEP tuner.

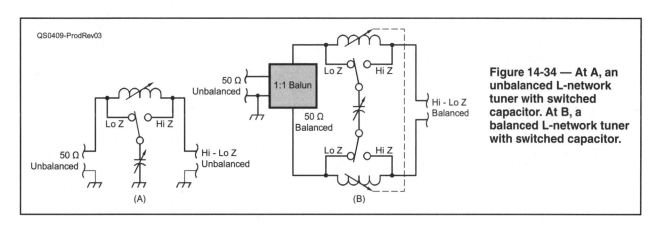

Figure 14-34 — At A, an unbalanced L-network tuner with switched capacitor. At B, a balanced L-network tuner with switched capacitor.

MFJ-974(H) Balanced Antenna Tuner

MFJ provides two versions of their '974, with ('974H) and without ('974) the capability to cover 160 meters. Both are rated at 300 W PEP, and 150 W CW. At only 7½ inches wide, it takes up a small amount of desk space. Interestingly, it has about the same shape as the old 275 W Johnson Matchbox, but is 1 to 2 inches smaller in each dimension. As noted above, this unit uses a T section design as in **Figure 14-33B**, so it is not necessary to switch capacitors from one side to the other as the impedance changes from high to low.

The inductor is varied by selecting among 12 steps. The H model has an extra inductance for 160 meters that changes the tuning range as needed. A cross-needle two-range (30 and 300 W full scale) power/SWR meter can be set to read peak or average power. Both the power level and null matched the meter on my transceiver quite closely. The capacitors are direct (1:1) drive, with plastic gearing between the ganged units. I found them easy to turn and to get a null. I used the old trick of tuning for maximum receive signal, first with the L switch, then with the capacitors.

MFJ provides a page of nominal settings by band that you may find helpful. When you switch to adjusting the tuner while transmitting, be sure to note their caution about not changing the inductor switch with power applied. You may burn the contacts otherwise. I also make it a practice to always tune at reduced power to avoid hitting my finals with a heavy mismatch at full power. When you have it set, turn up the power and confirm that all is well.

One caution that applies to all T section tuners is to note that multiple settings can result in low SWR. Unfortunately, some will have higher losses than others. The rule of thumb is to use the setting with the smallest inductance (the L switch position on

---

Table 14-15
MFJ-974H Balanced Antenna Tuner

Manufacturer's Specifications   *Measured in ARRL Lab*
Input load range: 12 to 2000 Ω.   See below.
Output SWR range: Not specified.   See below.
Frequency coverage: 1.8 to 54 MHz.   See below.
Input power: 150 W average, 300 W PEP.   Not tested.
Size: 6 × 7.5 × 9 inches (HWD).

SWR	Load (Ω)		160 Meters	80 Meters	40 Meters	20 Meters	10 Meters	6 Meters*
		Power Loss %	55	41	32	20	16	
8:1	6.25	SWR BW %	0.9	0.6	1.0	2.0	2.0	Not Tested
		Imbalance**	0	0	0	0	0	
		Power Loss %	40	33	23	<10	10	
4:1	12.5	SWR BW %	0.6	0.9	1.4	2.8	3.4	Not Tested
		Imbalance	0	0	0	0	0	
		Power Loss %	25	22	<10	<10	<10	
2:1	25	SWR BW %	0.8	1.1	3.2	4.9	2.4	Not Tested
		Imbalance	0	0	0	0	0	
		Power Loss %	22	15	32	20	<10	<10
1:1	50	SWR BW %	1.1	1.4	2.1	2.1	12	10
		Imbalance	0	0	0	0	0	0
		Power Loss %	18	<10	<10	<10	<10	
2:1	100	SWR BW %	1.1	1.7	4.1	7.0	25	Not Tested
		Imbalance	0	0	0	0	0	
		Power Loss %	17	<10	<10	<10	<10	
4:1	200	SWR BW %	1.1	2.8	2.5	9.1	10	Not Tested
		Imbalance	0	0	0	0	0	
		Power Loss %	12	<10	<10	<10	<10	
8:1	400	SWR BW %	1.5	3.4	7.5	7.0	3.7	Not Tested
		Imbalance	0	0	0	0	0	
		Power Loss %	10	<10	<10	<10	<10	
16:1	800	SWR BW %	1.9	4.3	8.3	7.7	3.7	Not Tested
		Imbalance	0	0	0	0	0	
		Power Loss %	<10	<10	<10	10	11	
32:1	1600	SWR BW %	2.1	2.6	5.6	4.4	3.0	Not Tested
		Imbalance	0	0	0	0	0	

Notes
Power losses are expressed as a percentage. A 10% power loss represents less than half (0.46) a dB.
The SWR bandwidth is the percentage of the measurement frequency that can be changed with the SWR staying under 1.5:1.
*The ARRL test fixture is only usable at 50 . on 6 meters.
**As defined in F. Witt, "Evaluation of Antenna Tuners and Baluns—An Update," *QEX*, Sep-Oct 2003, pp 3-14.

this tuner) and highest capacitance that will provide a match. One limitation of the switched rather than roller inductor is that you can't get values in between. I didn't find that much of a problem, as I was always able to get to 1.5:1 or better SWR with my antennas.

As you make adjustments, I suggest you log the settings for each frequency in a table such as the one supplied in the back of the manual. You may want to make photocopies or set up a spreadsheet so you will be able to repeat the process for your next antenna. If you find that you can't get a match at some frequency, try adding 6 feet of ladder line at a time. The different length will move the impedance around and may solve the problem, but you will have to retune on the other bands and hope to find a length that will tune properly on all bands.

Balanced loads are connected via standard (¾ inch) spaced multipurpose binding posts. These accept wire ends, or dual banana plugs, a handy connector for balanced feed lines at this power level. The '974H also provides a capability to match unbalanced loads and provides a coax

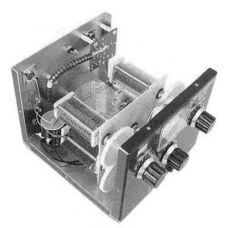

Figure 14-35 — MFJ-974H, inside view.

connector for that purpose. It is necessary to provide a jumper between the lower balanced load binding post and the ground terminal to complete the unbalanced hookup. Note that the output is not switched, so an antenna should be connected to either the coax connector or the balanced jacks, but not both.

Note that while the '974 is specified to match a wide range of impedances on 6 meters, neither the Lab nor W1ZR could test at any impedance other than 50 Ω. I tried

the unbalanced connection arrangement with my coax-fed G5RV. It worked fine until I tried it on 160 meters, not one of the bands the antenna is supposed to operate on. I was able to quickly find a match at low power. When I turned up the power past 70 W, arcing was evident inside the unit. I opened it up and was surprised to find that rather than the expected arcing tuner element, I found the arcing source was at the metering circuit board. Measured Lab data is shown in **Table 14-15**.

The unit went back to MFJ for repair under their warranty. Upon return, it worked fine at 100 W (my maximum power with the transceiver) and I was told by MFJ that a signal wire had been dressed too close to the meter board and arced. It was repositioned and MFJ installed the intended tie-wrap to hold it away from the meter board. The tuner was retested and had exhibited no problems.

Manufacturer: MFJ Enterprises Inc, 300 Industrial Park Rd, Starkville, MS 39759; tel 800-647-1800; fax 662-323-6551; **www. mfjenterprises.com**. 2004 price: MFJ-974, $179.95; MFJ-974H, $199.95.

Palstar AT4K Antenna Tuner

Unlike the other tuners in this review, the AT4K might best be described as an unbalanced tuner designed to feed unbalanced or balanced loads. This sounds contradictory, but really isn't, as described in footnotes 1 and 6. If you just think of this tuner as a "four-terminal black box" (see **Figure 14-33C**) connecting a balanced load to a balanced source, followed by a 1:1 balun going to the transceiver, you may get the picture.

An unbalanced T section, isolated from ground within the box, performs the required impedance transformation to match the impedance at the bottom of the balanced transmission line to 50 Ω to operate properly through the internal balun. This tuner also provides a heavy duty relay to connect the common points of the input, output and inductor to the chassis to convert it to a typical T section tuner for unbalanced loads.

An additional feature, not found in any of the other tuners in this review, is antenna switching capability. The AT4K has a single pair of balanced output terminals, but also has three coax outputs. Two can be tuned, or switched to straight through, while the third provides straight though operation only. This is a great spot to connect a dummy load, or a well matched Yagi.

The inside view gives a sense of the heavy duty construction of this massive tuner. The rotary inductor is fabricated from silver plated strip stock, rather than the usual wire, and the rolling contact is designed to grip a significant portion or the coil, not just the edge. The inductor is driven by a smooth turn-count dial reading out to $\frac{1}{10}$ of a turn and resetable in

---

Table 14-16
Palstar AT4K Balanced/Unbalanced Antenna Tuner

Manufacturer's Specifications   *Measured in ARRL Lab*
Input load range: 8 to 2000 Ω.   See below.
Output SWR range: Not specified.   See below.
Frequency coverage: 1.8 to 30 MHz.   See below.
Input power: 2500 W single tone.   Not tested.
Size: 5 × 15 × 16 inches (HWD).

SWR	Load (Ω)		160 Meters	80 Meters	40 Meters	20 Meters	10 Meters	6 Meters*
		Power Loss %	24	14	10	10	34	
8:1	6.25	SWR BW %	1.1	2.6	6.4	4.9	0.5	
		Imbalance	0.6	0.7	0	0.6	5.2	
		Power Loss %	12	<10	<10	<10	18	
4:1	12.5	SWR BW %	1.9	4.0	17	8.5	0.7	
		Imbalance	0	0.4	0	0.4	1.7	
		Power Loss %	<10	<10	<10	<10	<10	
2:1	25	SWR BW %	3.0	7.4	39	21	1.5	
		Imbalance	0	0.2	0	0.5	0	
		Power Loss %	<10	<10	<10	<10	<10	
1:1	50	SWR BW %	5.5	16	69	42	3.0	
		Imbalance	0.3	0	0	0.4	0.3	
		Power Loss %	<10	<10	<10	<10	37[1]	
2:1	100	SWR BW %	6.1	26	49	44	10	
		Imbalance	0.4	0	0	0	0	
		Power Loss %	<10	<10	<10	<10	Note 1	
4:1	200	SWR BW %	6.9	22	24	32	0.8	
		Imbalance	0.5	0	0	0	3.4	
		Power Loss %	<10	<10	<10	<10	Note 1	
8:1	400	SWR BW %	7.8	15	14	15		
		Imbalance	1.5	0.3	0	0		
		Power Loss %	<10	<10	<10	<10		
16:1	800	SWR BW %	7.2	10	10	8.5		
		Imbalance	2.6	0.5	0	0		
		Power Loss %	<10	<10	<10			
32:1	1600	SWR BW %	4.4	6.9	5.6	No Match	No Match	
		Imbalance	4.9	0	0			

Notes
[1]According to the owner's manual for the AT4K, the matching range is limited on 10 meters. In testing, it was found that matches (SWR <1.5:1) could be obtained on 10 meters with some higher impedance loads by using a large amount of inductance. However, it is very likely that the tuner was close to self-resonance under these conditions, and this type of operation should be avoided due to the high losses in the tuner.
Power losses are expressed as a percentage. A 10% power loss represents less than half (0.46) a dB.
The SWR bandwidth is the percentage of the measurement frequency that can be changed with the SWR staying under 1.5:1.

---

between marks. As with its sister units, the capacitors are driven by 5:1 reduction drives with 0 to 100 logging scales.

One design challenge with a tuner built of these large parts is to keep the minimum capacitance low enough so the unit will meet specifications at 10 meters. As shown in the data, Palstar has done a reasonably good job with this, but the limitations should be noted. I found that this unit could match all my antennas, balanced or

Figure 15-36 — Palstar AT4K, inside view.

unbalanced, except on 17 and 10 meters where not all impedances are within range. Again, a change in transmission line length may move your impedance to a value within the tunable range.

The metering was consistent with my other wattmeters, both in position of reflected null and forward power. I was able to easily return to a previous setting using the resolution of the dial scales. Measured Lab data is shown in **Table 14-16**.

Palstar AT1500BAL Balanced Antenna Tuner

The Palstar AT1500BAL is of the configuration shown in **Figure 14-34B**. It is a legal limit device and a look inside makes me believe that it can handle serious power. The rotary inductors, two edge-wound silver plated ball-bearing monsters, driven by a toothed fiberglass belt and turns counting dial take up a lot of the interior space. The rest is largely occupied by a 450 pF 4.5 kV variable driven by a smooth 5:1 vernier dial.

The inductors and capacitor are made in-house and work very well. I was particularly impressed with the resetability of the controls. The turns counter reads out to tenths of a turn,

Figure 14-37 — Palstar AT1500BAL, inside view.

and can be easily reset to ½ a tenth out of the 32 turns end-to-end. The vernier drive has a dial with 100 divisions and no perceivable backlash. Once you make up a table of

tuning values by frequency, retuning should be a snap. I found the tuner easy to use at W1ZR, matching all reasonable antenna configurations I tried. I am only able to test at the 500 W level and, as expected, encountered no difficulties.

The cross-needle meter (300 and 3000 W full scale ranges for forward average power) agreed closely with those on my equipment. One note, on many tuners, power is only required for meter lighting. On this unit, relays are used — both to switch capacitors from one end to the other and to switch in additional capacitance. The tuner will work only in the "high impedance/ no extra capacitance" mode if you neglect to plug in the

---

Table 14-17
Palstar AT1500BAL Balanced Antenna Tuner

Manufacturer's Specifications *Measured in ARRL Lab*
Input load range: 160 to 20 meters, 2500 ± j2500 Ω. See below.
20 meters 1000 ± j1000 Ω; 10 meters, 500 ± j500 Ω. See below.
Output SWR range: Not specified. See below.
Frequency coverage: 1.8 to 30 MHz. See below.
Input power: 1500 W PEP. Not tested.
Size: 6.5 × 12.5 × 15 inches (HWD).

SWR	Load (Ω)		160 Meters	80 Meters	40 Meters	20 Meters	10 Meters	6 Meters*
		Power Loss %	<10	<10	<10			
8:1	6.25	SWR BW %	No Match	No Match	9.9	6.6	5.4	
		Imbalance	0.3	0	0			
		Power Loss %	<10	<10	<10			
4:1	12.5	SWR BW %	No Match	No Match	1.3	1.3	10	
		Imbalance		0	0			
		Power Loss %	<10	<10	<10	17	<10	
2:1	25	SWR BW %	1.5	46	42	19	13	
		Imbalance	0	0	0	0	0	
		Power Loss %	<10	<10	<10	<10	<10	
1:1	50	SWR BW %	>100	>100	>100	>100	20	
		Imbalance	0.3	0	0	0	0	
		Power Loss %	<10	<10	<10	<10	<10	
2:1	100	SWR BW %	>100	54	58	56	61	
		Imbalance	0	0	0	0	0	
		Power Loss %	<10	<10	<10	<10	<10	
4:1	200	SWR BW %	>100	29	26	30	3.7	
		Imbalance	0.2	0	0	0	0	
		Power Loss %	<10	<10	<10	<10	13	
8:1	400	SWR BW %	17	23	18	20	1.7	
		Imbalance	0	0	0	0	0	
		Power Loss %	<10	<10	<10	<10	18	
16:1	800	SWR BW %	11	11	13	13	4.0	
		Imbalance	0	0	0	0	0	
		Power Loss %	<10	<10	<10	<10		
32:1	1600	SWR BW %	5.6	8.0	7.8	5	No Match	
		Imbalance	0	0	0	0		

Notes
Power losses are expressed as a percentage. A 10% power loss represents less than half (0.46) a dB.
The SWR bandwidth is the percentage of the measurement frequency that can be changed with the SWR staying under 1.5:1.

supplied wall-wart or connect an external 12 V dc supply. I found I needed to exercise both relays to tune my antenna on all bands.

Just after we purchased the AT1500BAL tuner for evaluation, Palstar added the AT1KBAL tuner to their line. In spite of their product numbers, they both are specified to handle the US legal limit. There is a key difference, however. The AT1KBAL tuner has the capacitors on the output side only. This results in a tuner that is designed to match from around 100 Ω up and is similar to an early balanced tuner described by Measures.[10,11]

Palstar has informed us that later this year they will replace the AT-1500BAL and the newer (and not tested) AT1KBAL with a new balanced tuner, the model BT1500A. This tuner will share the basic architecture and design of the AT1500BAL. It will make use of a new switched two-section variable capacitor designed to reduce minimum capacitance. This is intended to improve the tuning range, particularly on 10 meters. It will also have the inductors driven in tandem, removing the requirement for the drive belt and said to make for smoother tuning. Palstar expects to offer the BT1500A as their only balanced tuner once material for the others is exhausted. Measured Lab data is shown in **Table 14-17**.

Manufacturer: Palstar Inc, 9676 N Looney Rd, PO Box 1136, Piqua, OH 45356; tel 937-773-6255; fax 937-773-8003; **www.palstar.com**. 2004 prices: AT4K, $895; AT1500BAL, $695.95; AT1KBAL, $595.

E. F. Johnson Matchbox Antenna Tuners

Before WW II, the E. F. Johnson Company of Waseca, Minnesota, manufactured high quality variable capacitors, inductors and ceramic parts for electronics. By 1950 they were advertising their innovative Viking I transmitter in *The ARRL Radio Amateur's Handbook* and the next year their Matchbox antenna tuner for $48.95. A kW version was advertised in 1957. These tuners were based on the classic prewar balanced tuned circuit tuner (**Figure 14-32A**), but with an added twist. While the classic tuner of the day used plug-in coils to change bands, and manually attached tap points on the coil to change impedances, the Matchbox was bandswitching and had a unique differential capacitor arrangement to adjust the transformation ratio from the front panel, as shown in **Figure 14-32B**.

Models were available with and without SWR metering and the units included a TR relay useful for the typical separate transmitter and receiver setups of the day. By the '60s, the typical amateur antenna system had become one designed for resonant matched operation using coaxial cable without antenna tuners. Radios moved from AM to SSB, and Johnson changed their focus from amateur equipment to the commercial two-way FM radio market.

Their tuners are still a popular item at flea markets and on electronic auction sites. While not exactly a part of this review, Matchbox data reported by Witt in his earlier article is presented for comparison. As noted in the tables, the Matchbox tuners work well, but over a typically smaller impedance range than their modern counterparts. They also do not have band switch positions for any of the newer bands, although there is enough tuning range so they can typically cover 17 and 12, but not 30 or 60 meters. Within these limits, however, they can still be put to good use. Until the units discussed in this review became available, the Matchboxes were the only commercial tuner

---

Table 14-18

E. F. Johnson 275 W Matchbox, Balanced Antenna Tuner

Manufacturer's Specifications	*Measured in ARRL Lab*
Input load range: 25 to 1250 Ω.	See below.
Output SWR range: not specified.	See below.
Frequency coverage: 80, 40, 20, 15 and 10 meters	See below.
Input power: 275 W dc input.	Not tested.
Size: 7 × 10 × 10.5 inches (HWD).	

SWR	Load (Ω)		80 Meters	40 Meters	20 Meters	15 Meters	10 Meters
		Power Loss %					
4:1	12.5	SWR BW %	No Match	No Match	No Match	No Match	No Match
		Imbalance					
		Power Loss %				<10	<10
2:1	25	SWR BW %	No Match	No Match	No Match	4	4
		Imbalance				0	0
		Power Loss %	<10		<10	<10	<10
1:1	50	SWR BW %	2	No Match	>5	>5	3
		Imbalance	0	0	0	0	
		Power Loss %	<10	<10	12	11	<10
2:1	100	SWR BW %	2	4	>5	>5	3
		Imbalance	0	0	0	0	0
		Power Loss %	11	<10	<10	<10	11
4:1	200	SWR BW %	2	4	>5	>5	3
		Imbalance	0	0	0	0	0
		Power Loss %	12	<10	<10	<10	11
8:1	400	SWR BW %	2	4	>5	>5	3
		Imbalance	0	0	0	0	0
		Power Loss %	10	<10	<10	<10	11
16:1	800	SWR BW %	2	4	>5	>5	3
		Imbalance	0	0	0	0	0
		Power Loss %	10	<10			
32:1	1600	SWR BW %	2	4	No Match	No Match	No Match
		Imbalance	0	0			
		Power Loss %	10				
64:1	3200	SWR BW %	2	No Match			
		Imbalance	0				

Notes

Power losses are expressed as a percentage. A 10% power loss represents less than half (0.46) a dB.
The SWR bandwidth is the percentage of the measurement frequency that can be changed with the SWR staying under 1.5:1.

---

in wide use specifically designed to work with balanced antenna systems. Measured data from Frank Witt is shown in **Tables 14-18** and **14-19**.[12]

Notes

[1]R. D. Straw, Editor, *The ARRL Antenna Book,* 21st Edition. Available from your ARRL dealer or the ARRL Bookstore, ARRL order no. 9876. Telephone 860-594-0355, or toll-free in the US 888-277-5289; **www.arrl.org/shop**; **pubsales@ arrl.org**.

[2]The SG-235 is a 500 W version of the SG-230 with similar specifications, except needing a longer antenna. The SG-230 was reviewed in *QST* in November 1993.

[3]P. Pagel, "Product Review: Heath SA-2500 Antenna Tuner," *QST,* Mar 1985, pp 39-41.

[4]L. Aurick, "Product Review: J.W. Miller Automatic Antenna Tuner Auto-Trak Model AT2500," *QST,* Jul 1981, pp 42-43.

[5]S. Gerli, "Product Review: Daiwa CNA-1001 Automatic Antenna Tuner," *QST,* Nov 1981, pp 41-42.

[6]P. Danzer, N1II, "Open Wire Feed Line—A Second Look," *QST,* Apr 2004, pp 34-36.

[7]F. Witt, AI1H, "How to Evaluate Your Antenna Tuner—Parts 1 and 2," *QST,* Apr 1995, pp 30-34 and May 1995, pp 33-37.

[8]R. Lindquist, N1RL, "Product Review—QST Compares: Four High-Power Antenna Tuners," *QST,* Mar 1997, pp 73-77.

[9]R. D. Straw, Editor, *The ARRL Antenna Book,* 21st Edition. Available from your ARRL dealer or the ARRL Bookstore, ARRL order no. 9876. Telephone 860-594-0355, or toll-free in the US 888-277-5289; **www.arrl.org/shop**; **pubsales@ arrl.org**.

[10]Most center-fed antennas longer than 0.5 Ω are likely to meet this criterion. Very short antennas, or some low impedance driven arrays (8JK, for example) may have problems with this configuration, depending on feed line length.

[11]R. Measures, AG6K, "A Balanced Balanced Antenna Tuner," *QST,* Feb 1990, pp 28-32.

[12]See Note 7.

Table 14-19
E. F. Johnson kW Matchbox, Balanced Antenna Tuner

Manufacturer's Specifications
Input load range: 50 to 2000 Ω.
Output SWR range: not specified.
Frequency coverage: 80, 40, 20, 15 and 10 meters
Input power: 1000 W dc input.
Size: 12.5 × 17.25 × 11 inches (HWD).

Measured in ARRL Lab
See below.
See below.
See below.
Not tested.

SWR	Load (Ω)		80 Meters	40 Meters	20 Meters	15 Meters	10 Meters
		Power Loss %				15	<10
4:1	12.5	SWR BW %	No Match	No Match	No Match	1	3
		Imbalance				0	0
		Power Loss %			<10	13	<10
2:1	25	SWR BW %	No Match	No Match	2	2	4
		Imbalance			0	0	0
		Power Loss %		<10	<10	<10	<10
1:1	50	SWR BW %	No Match	2	2	2	4
		Imbalance		0	0	0	0
		Power Loss %	<10	<10	<10	<10	<10
2:1	100	SWR BW %	1	2	2	2	4
		Imbalance	0	0	0	0	0
		Power Loss %	<10	<10	11	<10	<10
4:1	200	SWR BW %	1	2	2	2	4
		Imbalance	0	0	0	0	0
		Power Loss %	<10	<10	<10	14	11
8:1	400	SWR BW %	1	2	2	2	4
		Imbalance	0	0	0	0	0
		Power Loss %	10	<10	<10	11	11
16:1	800	SWR BW %	1	3	2	2	4
		Imbalance	0	0	0	0	0
		Power Loss %	10	<10	<10		
32:1	1600	SWR BW %	1	2	2	No Match	No Match
		Imbalance	0	0	0		
		Power Loss %	10				
64:1	3200	SWR BW %	2	No Match	No Match	No Match	No Match
		Imbalance	0				

Notes
Power losses are expressed as a percentage. A 10% power loss represents less than half (0.46) a dB.
The SWR bandwidth is the percentage of the measurement frequency that can be changed with the SWR staying under 1.5:1.

Review Questions

14-1 What are some of the key issues to keep in mind if selecting a commercial tuner?

14-2 What is the major advantage of an automatic antenna tuner?

14-3 Why might it be important to use a remotely tuned antenna tuner near the antenna feed point?

Chapter 15

Building Your Own Tuners

Contents

Why Build a Tuner

A quick look at the schematic diagram of a basic manual antenna tuner (see Chapter 3), not counting metering and switching functions, reveals perhaps the simplest of amateur equipment schematics. A tuner has very few parts, and very few connections. That should make it easy to duplicate — and it does. Unfortunately each of the parts can be quite expensive and perhaps hard to find. On the other hand, if you have — or can easily obtain — the needed parts, there is no reason not to try building one or more tuners.

Special Purpose Tuners

Most of the tuners we have discussed heretofore have been of the general purpose variety. That is, they were designed to match varying loads on multiple frequencies from a single box. In any given amateur station, that may not be what is needed. You may have a need to match your particular antenna system to your particular radio on a particular frequency. That describes a "tuner" that needs no knobs or controls — just a fixed matching network.

The fixed network is more common than we may think. Every Yagi antenna with a gamma, T or hairpin match at the driven element has essentially done exactly that. Each is a matching network located at the antenna to provide a match from the antenna to the transmission line for a low loss run to the radio.

In a similar way, we can provide a network for each of our antennas that provides needed matching. The chapter title figure, a shot of a collection of specialized antenna matching systems at, W6TC, the advanced Amateur Radio station of the late George Badger, illustrates the point. None of those networks looks quite like any of the usual commercial antenna tuners of the last chapter! Another shot of this collection of networks, annotated with descriptions of each tuning element is shown in **Figure 15-1**.

Designing Your Special Purpose Tuner

While the usual circuit design and analysis tools of an electronic engineer can be used to design an impedance matching network, it can be a much simpler proposition for the amateur with a few software and hardware tools. The steps are straight-forward:

•*Determine the (complex) imped-ance that the antenna system will present to the radio or transmission line.*

Determining the impedance can be done in a number of ways. The best approach is probably to measure the impedance at the location that will have the tuner by using an antenna analyzer. Such analyzers include tun-

1 — RG-213 coax cable from shack to input of vacuum relay box behind board (37) to connect to SteppIR Yagi antenna or 30, 40, 60, 80 and 160 meter loop tuners.
2 — RG-213 coax cable to SteppIR antenna.
3 — Coax connector to 30 and 40 meter balun (38).
4 — 30 meter tuning inductor.
5 — 30 meter vacuum variable capacitor.
6 — 30/40 meter vacuum relay connected to loop.
7 — 30/40 meter vacuum relay connected to loop.
8 — 40 meter phone/CW vacuum relay.
9 — 40 meter phone/CW inductor.
10 — 40 meter tuning capacitor.
11 — Motor drive for 40 meter tuning capacitor.
12 — 40 meter tuning inductor.
13 — 40 meter matching inductor.
14 — Coax connector to 60 meter balun.
15 — 60 meter balun.
16 — 60 meter tuning inductor.
17 — 60 meter tuning vacuum variable capacitor.
18 — 60 meter vacuum relays.
19 — 80 meter coax connector to 80 meter balun.
20 — 80 meter balun.

21 — Motor drive for 80 meter vacuum variable capacitor.
22 — Limit switches for 80 meter vacuum variable capacitor.
23 — 80 meter vacuum variable capacitor.
24, 25 — 80 meter tuning and matching inductors.
26 — 80/160 meter vacuum relay.
27 — 160 meter open end vacuum relay.
28, 29 — Connection to loop on tower.
30 — 160 meter receive vacuum relay.
31-33 — 160 meter receive RC network.
34 — Spark gap protector for 160 meter receive RC network.
35, 36 — 25-pair control cable to shack.
37 — Vacuum relay switch box to connect to SteppIR Yagi or loop.
38 — 30 and 40 meter balun.
39, 40 — Feed-through to 80 and 160 meter radial system.
41 — Remote motor control.
42 — Control shaft for 30 meter vacuum variable capacitor (5).
43 — Motor control relay.
44 — 160 meter balun.
45 — Manual control for 60 meter vacuum variable capacitor.
46 — Connector to 160 meter balun.

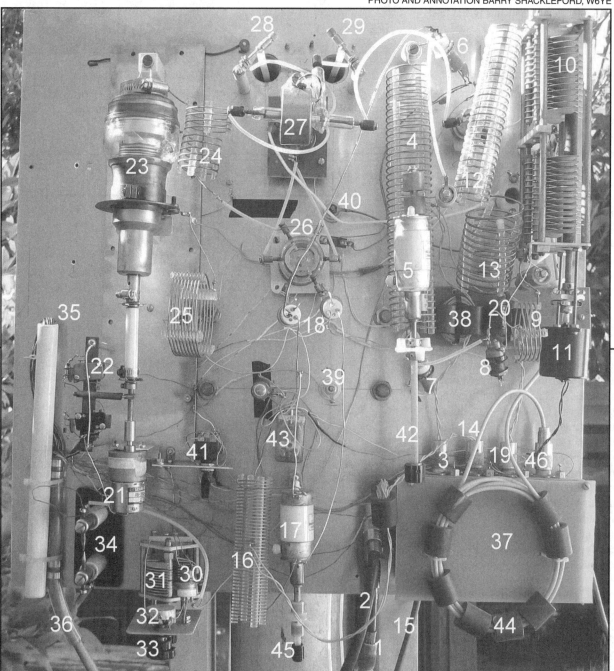

Figure 15-1 — Example of perhaps the extreme in homemade antenna tuning arrangements. This collection of remotely controlled special purpose antenna tuners, all on an outside panel (cover removed for photo), was made to switch between and tune the multiple antenna systems of the late George Badger, W6TC, the designer and builder. The annotations refer to the elements in the list below.

The tuner panel includes separate remote controlled matching networks and connections for each of the HF bands from 30 to 160 meters. It is mounted at the base of the tower. At the top of the tuner panel are two connectors that connect to the two lower ends of the 30, 40, 60, 80 and 160 meter loop that extends from the left connector up to the 5 foot fiberglass boom extension on the left, up and over the 8 foot fiberglass mast extension at the top to the boom extension on the right, then down to the right connector.

able RF generators and displays that indicate actual complex (resistive and reactive) impedance, not just SWR. These are available from a number of manufacturers for a few hundred dollars, and are a valuable tool for the antenna inclined amateur. **Figure 15-2** shows a sampling that were tested for a *QST* product review.[1]

Some analyzers provide the resistive value of the impedance and the magnitude, but not the sign of the reactive part. In order to design a matching network, it is important to know whether the reactance is positive (inductive) or negative (capacitive). Fortunately, it is usually easy to determine this. Just make a slight change in frequency and note the change in the value of reactance. If the reactance goes up as the frequency goes up it is inductive (+). If it goes down with increasing frequency, it is capacitive (–). This only works if the reactance does not go to zero between the two data points. Note that many programs use a lower case italicized letter *j* as part of the reactive value. This indicates that it should be mathematically considered perpendicular to the resistive value, or calculated as if an imaginary number. Don't let this bother you if it is not a familiar concept.

Another approach is to use antenna modeling software to determine the antenna, or the antenna system, impedance. The procedure I will outline will work with either. While modeling will result in a reasonable estimate of the impedance, it is rare that it provides an exact result, since generally not all conditions (ground parameters, for example) are fully known. This is what I did in the example that follows.

A third approach is to rely on manufacturers' or other published data. This also has its limitations in terms of the effect of the actual conditions at your location.

Figure 15-3 provides the basis for a short example of how this process can easily be conducted. The antenna under consideration is a dipole cut for the low end of the 40 meter amateur band. Instead of feeding it directly

1Notes appear on page 11.

Figure 15-2 — A sampling of hand held antenna analyzers from Autek, Kuranishi, MFJ and Palstar.

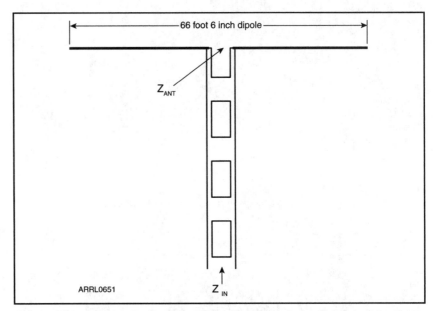

Figure 15-3 — 40 meter dipole used as the example for the determination of a special purpose matching network.

with coax, which would likely not require a matching network, we have selected to use 70 feet of nominal 450 Ω window line, so it can be fed efficiently on multiple bands. In order to use it on 40 meters, we determine (using *EZNEC* antenna modeling software) that the impedance at the center and each end of the band at the antenna feed point is as shown in **Table 15-1**.[2]

We then use the transmission line analysis program *TLW*, furnished with recent editions of *The ARRL Antenna Book*, to determine the impedance at the bottom of the mismatched transmission line as shown in **Table 15-2**.[3] Note that we could have gone directly to Table 15-2 using many antenna

analysis programs that are equipped with transmission line models. My version of *EZNEC* included an early transmission line capability that did not take losses into account, so I used *TLW* instead. Since we need *TLW* for the next step, it wasn't any extra effort. One hint about using *TLW* — when finished don't just close the program window — click on the EXIT button to avoid problems with it starting properly next time.

•*Design a network that will transform the impedance to the desired impedance of the radio or transmission line.*

There are many techniques that could be employed to design a matching network to match any of the im-

Table 15-1

Impedance Predicted at the Antenna (Z_{ANT}) as Shown in Figure 15-1.

Frequency(MHz)	Resistive Part (Ω)	Reactive Part (Ω)	50 Ω SWR
7.0	82.3	−34.0	2.0
7.15	88.0	−0.37	1.8
7.3	94.1	+33.1	2.2

Table 15-2

Impedance Predicted at Bottom of the 70 Foot Transmission Line (Z_{IN}) as Shown in Figure 15-1.

Frequency(MHz)	Resistive Part (Ω)	Reactive Part (Ω)	450 Ω SWR
7.0	87.7	+82.9	4.9
7.15	103.3	+148.6	4.6
7.3	236.5	+229.7	4.3

pedances in Table 15-2 to our desired 50 Ω transmitter. Perhaps the easiest is to just click the TUNER button on the *TLW* screen shown in **Figure 15-4**. The screen shown in **Figure 15-5** will then appear, providing a place to input some common parameters including transmitter power and physical component properties.

While the design power is a straightforward parameter, some of the other terms may not be. The inductor and capacitor Q are related to the losses in the components. Typically, the biggest loss in an HF tuner, especially one with an air dielectric

capacitor(s), is due to coil wire resistance. If you are buying a coil, it will likely specify the Q. If not, you can measure the impedance of the coil on your antenna analyzer at the operating frequency. The Q is just X_L/R, both available on an antenna analyzer screen.[4] Values in the hundreds are typical, and the good news is the program results are not very sensitive to the value of Q. A 100% change in Q, in this example, results in less than a 0.5% change in the value of the specified inductor and capacitor — smaller than the usual component tolerance, thus we specify a Q of 200 and the

resulting design should be fine for most real inductors.

The OUTPUT STRAY CAPACITANCE value represents the capacitance of the wiring and components on the output side to the chassis. All wiring and components in the usual metal chassis or cabinet have capacitance to the metal walls. This is most important as the frequency goes up. Values in the tens of picofarads are common depending largely on component size and placement.

The other choice on this screen is the TUNER NETWORK TYPE. There really isn't too much to say about this — pick the one you like best, or better yet — try them all. I am somewhat partial to the low-pass L-network because it only has two components and provides some attenuation of harmonic signals. It also has only one solution for any load — more later. Pick any one to start, you will likely want to look at them all to find which one has components that are available or easiest to obtain.

If you pick any configuration besides the L-network, it will ask you for a value to use for the capacitor on the output side (towards antenna). It will try to design a tuner for any value you pick. If it can't make a tuner work with your value it will suggest making it larger or smaller. Make note of the power loss and try different values of output capacitor

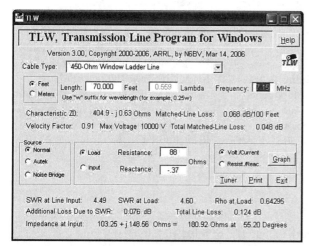

Figure 15-4 — Input screen of *TLW* transmission line analysis software used to determine the impedance at the bottom of the mismatched transmission line of Figure 15-1.

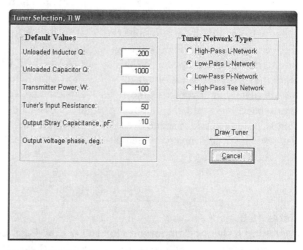

Figure 15-5 — Antenna tuner Input screen of *TLW* software. Note the tuner configuration selected, LOW-PASS L-NETWORK, the power level, 100 W, that determines component ratings as well as the other parameters as described in the text.

until you achieve a design that has an acceptable amount of loss and reasonably sized components. This illustrates the fact that the three element tuners — Pi- and T-network — have more than one set of adjustments that will provide a satisfactory match to the radio. Unfortunately, while they will all look good to the radio, some will have more loss than others.

Push the DRAW TUNER button. The screen shown in **Figure 15-6** should appear providing the design details for the low-pass L-network tuner I selected. In addition to the component values needed to provide the match, the table above the schematic provides information on component stress levels and other key data. The primary selection criterion can be found by looking at the resulting tuner designs (next paragraph) in each configuration and seeing which ones have component values that are reasonable, and even better, that you have on hand. A look at the resulting efficiency, expressed as POWER INTO LOAD, may also help you select a preferred topology.

Table 15-3 shows the resulting design for the middle and both edges of the 40 meter band. This design can be used as a starting point for a single frequency, single load, matching network. I say starting point because even with careful analysis there are a few variables that are not known exactly, including actual component values — typical tolerances are ±10% — for example. This is often taken into account by making one or both components variable, or trying slightly different component values until the desired result is obtained.

Alternately, if coverage of the entire band is desired, the components could be made variable over the ranges shown. It is also possible that

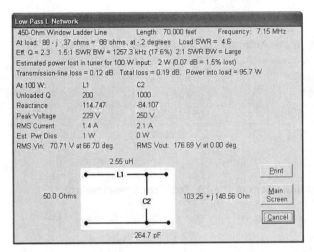

Figure 15-6 — Antenna tuner output (design) screen of *TLW* software. Note the tuner schematic with parts values shown. The data and table above provide additional important information.

the values for the middle of the band will provide a satisfactory match over at least a portion of a band without requiring change. This can be determined by trial and error, or simulated in an antenna analysis program by using modeled lumped "loads" at the bottom of the transmission line.

•*Build and test the network.*

As noted, the hardest part is often finding the needed components, especially those needed for high power networks. Hamfest flea markets are often a good source for such items, although they often come with a level of uncertainty regarding ancestry and component value. Again, the trusty antenna analyzer can be used to measure the reactance. Fixed or tapped inductors can be easily wound using plastic rod or tubing as a form. *The ARRL Handbook* provides a source of formulae for winding the desired inductance.

As with all RF projects, keep leads short and direct. To minimize stray capacitance, keep the components some distance from the cabinet edges. Use high quality connectors and make sure you have provided direct

connectivity for all needed interconnections.

The best way to test the network is to start with the antenna analyzer. With the network connected to the proper place on the transmission line, the impedance should read close to 50 Ω at the design frequency. Now take *swept frequency* type data by measuring the impedance and SWR every 25 or 50 kHz. By plotting these on a graph, you should have a good idea of what the network will do and whether or not it will work across the range. If it isn't quite right, make a small change in one value and repeat the sweep. You should see an indication of the extent and direction of the change. Since there are only two or three components, you should quickly converge on your result.

Next hook it to your radio tuned to an unused frequency and note the transceiver's SWR reading. It should be close to that of the analyzer. Slowly increase the power to just below the level you designed to. Turn off the transmitter and check to see if any components have become hot — they shouldn't!

Table 15-3

Matching Network Components for 100 W Low-Pass L-Network to Match Z of Table 15-2 to 50 Ω.

Frequency(MHz)	Inductance (µH)	Inductor Current (A_p)	Capacitance (pF)	Capacitor Voltage (V_p)	Efficiency (%)
7.0	1.72	1.4	339.4	181	96.1
7.15	2.55	1.4	264.7	250	95.7
7.3	3.28	1.4	205.2	317	95.4

160 and 80 Meter Matching Network for Your 43 Foot Vertical — *Part 1*

The popular 43 foot vertical works best with matching at the antenna base — here's a way to do it for our two MF bands.

Phil Salas, AD5X

I've recently made the move to a 43 foot vertical for much of my lower frequency operations. This length antenna offers higher radiation resistance than shorter loaded monopoles. Increased radiation resistance improves efficiency by reducing the effects of ground losses, especially when you have an electrically short antenna — a characteristic of even a 43 foot antenna on 160 and 80 meters. If fed with a 1:4 unbalanced to unbalanced transformer (unun), a 43 foot antenna has a reasonable compromise SWR on 60 through 10 meters, which means that cable and unun losses are pretty much negligible on these bands.

This antenna is really not a good performer on 160 meters, and to a lesser extent on 80 meters, unless you provide matching right at the antenna base. This is due to the high capacitive reactance and still relatively low radiation resistance of a 43 foot antenna on 160 and 80 meters. This makes the mismatch so bad that it is almost impossible to efficiently match from your shack. If you can match the antenna system from your shack, you will throw away a lot of power in your coax and unun due to the very bad mismatch at the antenna.

I thus started experimenting with matching networks and wound up with two external impedance matching devices designed to significantly reduce SWR related coax losses and unun mismatch losses, and to help the inside tuner match on 160 and 80 meters. This month we'll look at the simpler version of the two matching networks. This version requires manual insertion of the matching network whenever you want to operate on 80 or 160 meters.

The Matching Requirement

According to my AIM4170C antenna analyzer, my 43 foot vertical antenna has a capacitive reactance of about 580 Ω on 160 meters. This will vary based on the particular construction of your 43 foot vertical, its proximity to other objects, and other fac-

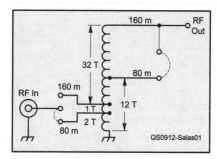

Figure 1 — Schematic diagram of the two band matching unit. 80 meter connections shown with dashed lines.

Figure 2 — T400A-2 160 and 80 meter matching unit.

tors. The reactance will almost certainly be in the 550 to 650 Ω range. This amount of capacitive reactance needs approximately 50 μH of inductance in order to resonate the antenna. On 80 meters, approximately 9 μH is needed to resonate the antenna. A 50 μH high Q inductor is going to be large. For this first solution, I elected to go with a toroidal inductor in order to keep the matching unit as compact as possible.

Toroid Inductor Matching Solution

This compact design will handle the full legal limit on 80 and 160 meters for low duty cycle SSB and CW modes. The inductor consists of 35 turns of #14 AWG solid copper insulated house wiring wound on a T400A-2 toroid core. The antenna feed point is tapped two turns from the ground end for 80 meters, and three turns from the ground end for 160 meters. You should start with 38 turns total on your toroid, but then remove turns as necessary to get the network to resonate where you want it in the 160 meter band (more on this later).

I mounted the toroid assembly in a 6 × 6 × 4 inch NEMA enclosure using a 2½ inch long #10 machine screw and associated hardware along with a 2 × 4 inch piece of unplated fiberglass PC board material. Before you mount the toroid, prepare

---

Table 1
160 Meter Toroid Impedance Matching Assembly Parts List

Description	Source/Part Number*
Banana plug (4 required)	Mouser 174-R802-EX
Binding post, black (4 required)	Mouser 164-R126B-EX
Binding post, red	Mouser 164-R126R-EX
NEMA Enclosure, 6 × 6 × 4 inch	Lowes/Home Depot
Glass cloth tape, 3M #27	ACE Hardware
SO-239 connector	Mouser 601-25-7350
Toroid, T400A-2 powdered iron	Amidon T400A-2

*Amidon parts are available from **www.amidoncorp.com** and Mouser parts from **www.mouser.com**.

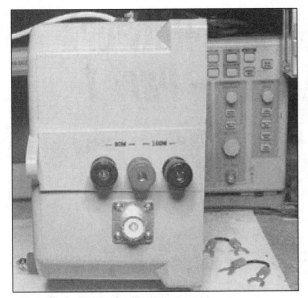

Figure 3 — 160 and 80 meter input tap points.

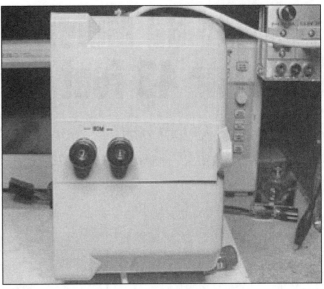

Figure 4 — 80 meter coil shorting jacks.

it by scraping the insulation off the outside second, third and 11th through 13th wire turns. Because of the high voltages possible at legal limit power levels, especially on 160 meters, wrap the toroid with two layers of 3M #27 glass cloth electrical tape for added insulation between the #14 AWG wires and the toroid core.

Figure 1 is the schematic of the matching assembly, Figure 2 shows the internal details of the assembly, and Table 1 lists the parts necessary. To select between 160 and 80 meter operation, I used external jumpers across binding posts as shown in Figures 3 and 4. Stainless steel #8 hardware (screws, washers, lockwashers and nuts) are used for the matching unit ground and RF output terminals. Internal to the matching unit, I used a 2 inch wide strip of aluminum duct repair tape as a good low impedance ground between the UHF connector and the ground screw on the bottom of the case. Finally, I used #14 AWG stranded insulated wire for all internal connections.

Tuning the Matching Network to Resonance

Your particular installation will almost certainly require you to change the resonant frequency of the matching network. This is because there will be some variations of the antenna impedance based on your particular antenna physical construction, proximity to other objects and final length, as well as your desired operating frequency range. The design is such that the overall inductance is too large for 160 meters, so the network should resonate at or below the lower band edge. Therefore, you will need to remove one or more of the upper inductor turns in order to resonate the network for the desired frequency on 160 meters.

To do this, first solder wires from the second and third turn tap points on the coil to the two outer binding posts by the SO-239 connector. The input tap points tend to be fairly noncritical and will probably be the same for all installations. Now solder a short wire from the SO-239 center pin to the middle binding post. Next, externally jumper the

middle binding post to the 160 meter binding post (third turn).

Connect the matching assembly to the base of your 43 foot vertical and see where the minimum SWR point is on 160 meters using your antenna analyzer. If the resonant frequency is too low, remove a turn of wire and see where the minimum SWR point is again. You'll see about a 50 kHz upward move in frequency per turn of wire removed. When you have your desired resonant point on 160 meters, it is time to move to 80 meters. Externally jumper the input tap middle binding post to the 80 meter binding post (second turn), and use a clip lead to short from the top of the coil to turn number 12 and see where your minimum SWR frequency occurs. Move the tap point up or down until your resonance point (lowest SWR) is where you want it. Solder a wire from this tap point to one of the binding posts. Solder another wire from the top of the coil to another binding post. Now you will be able to externally jumper these binding posts to select either 160 or 80 meters.

My final test results for 160 and 80 meters are shown in Figures 5 and 6 as measured with my RigExperts AA-200 antenna analyzer connected directly to the matching network input at the base of the antenna. I'm a CW operator, so I favor resonance in the lower part of these bands, but you can adjust for your favorite portion of each band. The 2:1 SWR bandwidth on 160 meters is about 50 kHz, and about 150 kHz on 80 meters. Even a 3:1 SWR on these bands results in negligible SWR related cable losses for any reasonable length cable and is easily matched with my MFJ-998 in-shack tuner or most transceivers' internal tuners.

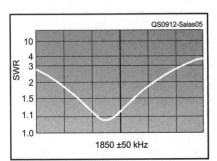

Figure 5 — Measured SWR across 160 meters indicating a 2:1 SWR bandwidth of approximately 50 kHz.

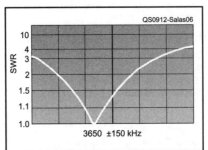

Figure 6 — SWR across 80 meters indicating a measured 2:1 SWR bandwidth of about 150 kHz.

Figure 7 — Matching unit at the base of the author's 43 foot antenna. In this view, it is strapped for 80 meters.

antenna at the same time, and just leave off the ground wire from the unit that is not used. The matching unit connected to the base of my 43 foot vertical is shown in Figure 7.

Conclusion

The matching network discussed in this article will permit very effective operation of your 43 foot vertical on the 160 and 80 meter bands. In Part 2, we'll look at a remotely switchable 160, 80 and 60 through 10 meter base matching unit. It is more complex, but it is also more convenient. Until then, see you on top band!

Amateur Extra class operator and ARRL Life Member Phil Salas, AD5X, was first licensed as WN3BCQ in 1964. Ham radio became the reason he subsequently pursued a career in electrical engineering. Phil earned BSEE and MSEE degrees from Virginia Tech and SMU, respectively, and worked in new product development for the next 33 years. Phil is now retired and spends his days split between ham radio related projects and enjoying time with his wife, Debbie, N5UPT. You can reach Phil at 1517 Creekside Dr, Richardson, TX 75081 or at **ad5x@arrl.net**.

Operation

Using the matching unit is simple. Just disconnect your normal unun when you want to operate on 160 or 80 meters and connect this matching unit to the base of the antenna. Select either 160 or 80 meters with the external straps. You can connect both the unun and this matching unit to the

160 and 80 Meter Matching Network for Your 43 Foot Vertical — *Part 2*

This dual band matching section design provides for remote band changing.

Phil Salas, AD5X

In Part 1, I described a simple 160 and 80 meter base matching assembly for a 43 foot antenna. While that unit is very effective and inexpensive to build, it is also a little inconvenient in that you must connect it when it is needed, and you must also manually enable 160 or 80 meter operation using straps. This month, we'll look at a more versatile matching assembly that is completely remote-controllable for operation on all bands. Again, this base matching network will significantly eliminate SWR-related coax losses and unun mismatch losses, and assist inside tuners in providing a match on 160 and 80 meters.

The All Band Matching Solution

As discussed in Part 1,[1] a 43 foot vertical antenna requires approximately 50 μH of inductance to resonate the antenna. On 80 meters, approximately 9 μH is needed for resonance. For the matching solution shown in Figure 1, I used an MFJ 404-0669 air wound coil and two Array Solutions RF-30 relays for up to full legal limit matching on all bands from 160 to 10 meters. A 2.1 × 5.5 mm dc power jack located below the SO-239 connector provides for relay control voltage inputs of 0 V, +12 or –12 V dc. The control input MOVs and bypass capacitors are mounted on a 6 terminal strip inside the matching assembly.

The matching unit operates as follows: With no control voltage applied, the inductor is disconnected and the unun is connected across the antenna feed point thereby preserving the original compromise SWR on 60-10 meters.

When +12 V is applied, the inductor is connected across the antenna feed point and inductor turns are shorted to resonate the antenna on 80 meters.

When the voltage is reversed, the short across the coil is removed and the matching section resonates the antenna on 160 meters. In both the 160 and 80 meter cases, the unun secondary taps into the inductor at the 200 Ω point, providing a proper match to the unun on these bands. This keeps the unun second-

[1]Notes appear on page 35.

ary voltage reasonable, and the feed line and unun losses very low as well.

I built the matching unit into an 8 × 8 × 4 inch NEMA weatherproof box available from home supply stores (see Figure 2). This box is too small to fit the entire inductor length needed, so I split the inductor into two pieces as can be seen in Figure 1. The long inductor section consists of 61 turns, and the short inductor section consists of 12 turns. While I preferred the more compact size of this box, you may wish to use the larger 12 × 12 × 4 inch NEMA box that can contain the full uncut inductor length needed.

All internal wiring uses insulated #14 AWG stranded wire. I attached the wires to the coil tap points using the MFJ coil clips called out in the parts list. You can solder the wires directly to the coil, but this is difficult due to the #12 AWG size of the coil wire and the spacing of the turns. The coil is mounted with #8 stainless steel screws, washers, lock washers and nuts also used for the ground and antenna feed terminals. Figure 1 shows the final matching unit with all components mounted. Note the terminal strip with the MOVs and bypass capacitors.

Since the antenna is unbalanced, a current balun or voltage unun is typically used. A voltage unun should be wired as shown in Figure 2.

Relay Connections

Some comments are necessary regarding the relay connections. See the sidebar on the *QST* binaries Web site for a discussion of how high the peak voltage across the full coil can be on 160 meters. As you can see, I connected relay contacts in series to increase the overall breakdown voltage. Also, the tap points on the inductor provide additional voltage above ground, which helps with the overall breakdown voltage.

The main concern is with the contact-to-coil 5.3 kV peak breakdown rating. When I examined the relays, I observed that the outer SPDT contacts are connected via insulated internal wires that are well separated from the coil by 0.1 to 0.2 inches. The problem is with the center SPDT relay common wire, which is in contact with the coil. While the coil and common wire are both insulated, there is no air-gap separation between them. This common wire-to-coil contact is obviously what

Figure 1 — All parts mounted in the NEMA enclosure.

determines the breakdown voltage rating. The way I got around this problem was to use the center SPDT relay contacts for the lowest potential interfaces as indicated in the schematic (Figure 2).

For the switched control voltage input, I used a 12 V, 1 A wall wart to keep the +12 V control voltages separate and isolated from the regular station voltage. This is to eliminate any possibility of shorting the main power supply when the control voltage polarity is flipped.

I mounted the switch in a small plastic box that I attached to my transceiver support shelf. The unlabeled center-off position is for 60 through 10 meter operation. The separate switch you see in the photo is for controlling other outdoor accessories, as I have two voltage feeds going out to my antenna location.

Matching Network Resonance

As with the previous matching network, you will almost certainly need to adjust the resonant frequency of the matching network due to variations in particular antenna physical construction, proximity to other objects and final length, as well as your desired operating frequency range. The overall starting inductance is too large for 160 meters, so the network will resonate at or below the lower band edge. Therefore, you can simply short one or more of the upper (short coil) inductor turns in order to tune the network higher to your desired 160 meter frequency.

To do this, first leave off the wire leads that attach between the relay contacts and the tap points on the coil. Build up short jumpers

Figure 3 — The completed all band remotely controlled switching and impedance matching network mounted at the antenna base.

using the test-clips and micro-clips (perfect for the coil turn taps) called out in the parts list, and attach these between the relay contacts and coil, using the suggested tap points shown on the schematic.

Connect the matching assembly to the base of your 43 foot vertical (see Figure 3). Then enable 160 meter operation by applying –12 V dc, and jumper turns on the 12 turn inductor with a short clip lead until you find your desired 160 meter resonance point. Next, move the 160 meter relay tap point until you get minimum SWR. Now permanently short the turns on the short coil by soldering a piece of #16 AWG buss wire across these turns.

As you can see from my photos, I needed to short six turns on this coil. Next enable 80 meter operation (apply +12 V to the relays

assembly) and select the coil shorting point for your desired resonant frequency and the tap point for best SWR. Finally remove the test clips leads, attach the coil clips, and solder wires between the coil clips and relay.

The 2:1 SWR bandwidth on 160 meters is about 50 kHz, and about 150 kHz on 80 meters. Even a 4:1 SWR on these bands results in negligible SWR related cable and unun loss, and is easily matched with my MFJ-998, an in-shack tuner.

Operation

Operation of this matching unit couldn't be simpler. When no control voltage is applied, the antenna functions as it always has on 60 through 10 meters. For 80 meter operation, apply +12 V dc, and for 160 meter operation apply –12 V dc. The matching unit connected to the base of my 43 foot vertical is shown in Figure 10.

Conclusion

The matching network discussed in this article will permit very effective operation of your 43 foot vertical on all bands from 160 through 10 meters. Although on 10, 12 and 15 meters the elevation angle of the peak is higher than optimum for DX, it will still allow contacts. Feel free to experiment a little. You might prefer to use the toroid from Part 1 in this design instead of the air-core inductor. If you are not running more than about 500 W, the less expensive RF-10 relays are all you will need. Have fun, and I'll see you on the low bands.

Notes
[1]P. Salas, AD5X, "160 Meter Matching Network for Your 43 Foot Vertical — *Part 1*," *QST*, Dec 2009, pp 30-32.
[2]**www.arrl.org/files/qst-binaries**.

See Part 1 for Phil's bio. You can reach Phil at 1517 Creekside Dr, Richardson, TX 75081 or at **ad5x@arrl.net**.

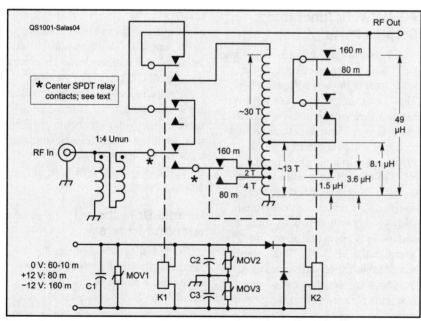

Figure 2 — Schematic of the remotely controlled matching network. The parts list is on the QST binaries version.[2]

Home Built General Purpose Tuners

There are a number of approaches to the design and construction of general purpose antenna tuners. Perhaps the easiest is to replicate existing successful designs, although finding the exact parts called for is sometimes a problem. Fortunately, the exact values are not very critical. It is also possible, if somewhat tedious, to go through the *TLW* based procedure described above at the extremes of frequency and mismatch to determine the range of values needed and then construct a tuner with variable and/or switched elements, often in combination, that will cover the needed range.

I have done this for the most popular configurations, see **Figure 15-7**, the high-pass T-network, Pi-network and low pass L-network with the results shown in **Tables 15-4** through **15-6**. I have provided the values for matching loads with a 10:1 SWR, the usual spec for a wide range tuner. In addition to the resistive loads at 5 and 500 Ω, I have made runs for moderate reactive loads of $25 \pm j25$ Ω and extreme reactive loads of $250 \pm j250$ Ω, all with approximately a 10:1 SWR.

As noted in Chapter 4, the Pi- and T-network tuners have multiple solutions for any load, while the L-network has a single solution. It is worth stressing this in case you use one, whether a commercial unit or a home-built one. Look again at Table 4-1, in Chapter 4, to get the idea.

Such "HF" tuners sometimes include the MF 160 meter amateur band as well as the 80 through 10 meter HF bands. I have provided data for 160, 80 and above the top of 10 meters so you can decide which way you want to go. Note that the addition of 160 meters makes a big difference in the component values required, one reason it often is not included. In addition, in some cases the larger inductor and capacitor(s) may have too high a minimum value to allow proper operation on 10 meters.

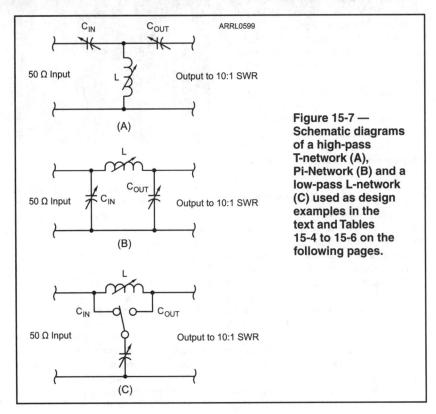

Figure 15-7 — Schematic diagrams of a high-pass T-network (A), Pi-Network (B) and a low-pass L-network (C) used as design examples in the text and Tables 15-4 to 15-6 on the following pages.

A T-Network Tuner from Surplus Parts

A T-network tuner that I made some years back and used effectively for some time is shown in **Figure 15-8**. This is an example of a "use what you have and see what it does" approach to tuner design. The unit is built around a chassis and panel from a WW2 surplus plug in tuning unit from a BC-375 transmitter used in bomber aircraft. The capacitor controls nice 4:1 planetary drives with calibrated scales, along with the rotary indicator and its turns count dial also came from a cannibalized BC-375. Today they would all be preserved as antiques, but in 1965, they were sources of cheap or free parts for new transmitting equipment.

Figure 15-9 shows the inside of the tuner, including a home built "Moni-

match Mark II" type SWR indicator, along with a battery holder for the meter amplifier.[5] Modern transceivers include SWR indication, so these may no longer be needed. The variable capacitors, one above the other on the right side, were of a few hundred pF each, and the rotary inductor (on left) was probably around 15 µH. In those days, no one knew for sure — but it successfully matched any of my antennas for years.

Simple Breadboard Antenna Tuners

Home-built antenna tuners don't need to be as mechanically complex as my old T-match. Barry Shackleford, W6YE, has constructed a few using available variable capacitors and inductors fabricated in his workshop. While these won't handle full power,

Table 15-4

Component Requirements for High-Pass (Shunt L) T-Network Antenna Tuners at 10:1 SWR

Frequency/Z (Ω) 1.8 MHz	Capacitor Input (pF)	Output (pF)	Inductor (µH)	Capacitor Voltage (V_p) 100 W	1500 W	Efficiency (%)
5	1136	3000	2.1	180	710	96
500	548	500	13.9	323	1250	98
25 + j100	343	300	10.3	790	3070	92
25 − j100	170	300	20	1040	4030	86
250 + j250	308	200	10.5	380	1470	98
250 − j250	337	300	16.9	525	2030	96
Frequency/Z (Ω) 3.5 MHz	Capacitor Input (pF)	Output (pF)	Inductor (µH)	Capacitor Voltage (V_p) 100 W	1500 W	Efficiency (%)
5	563	1500	1.1	190	720	96
500	265	200	7.3	343	1330	98
25 + j100	275	200	3.5	613	2373	95
25 − j100	104	200	8.6	880	3403	88
250 + j250	333	100	5.6	381	1475	98
250 − j250	136	100	10.8	670	2600	94
Frequency/Z (Ω) 30 MHz	Capacitor Input (pF)	Output (pF)	Inductor (µH)	Capacitor Voltage (V_p) 100 W	1500 W	Efficiency (%)
5	79	200	0.12	160	640	96
500	29	50	0.77	370	1470	97
25 + j100	91	30	0.24	400	1560	98
25 − j100	24	100	0.46	440	1710	93
250 + j250	36	100	0.9	300	1150	98
250 − j250	29	100	0.6	360	1410	97

Table 15-5

Component Requirements for Low-Pass (Series L) L-Network Antenna Tuners at 10:1 SWR

Frequency/Z (Ω) 1.8 MHz	Capacitor Input (pF)	Output (pF)	Inductor (µH)	Capacitor Voltage (V_p) 100 W	1500 W	Efficiency (%)
5	5254	n/a	1.34	100	390	98
500	n/a	536	13.5	310	1210	98
25 + j100	n/a	1408	12	290	1120	98
25 − j100	1760	n/a	11	100	390	97
250 + j250	n/a	713	13	310	1210	98
250 − j250	n/a	359	13	310	1210	98
Frequency/Z (Ω) 3.5 MHz	Capacitor Input (pF)	Output (pF)	Inductor (µH)	Capacitor Voltage (V_p) 100 W	1500 W	Efficiency (%)
5	2700	n/a	0.69	100	400	98
500	n/a	275	6.8	310	1200	98
25 + j100	n/a	720	6.2	290	1120	98
25 − j100	926	n/a	5.6	100	390	97
250 + j250	n/a	367	6.8	310	1210	98
250 − j250	n/a	184	6.8	310	1210	98
Frequency/Z (Ω) 30 MHz	Capacitor Input (pF)	Output (pF)	Inductor (µH)	Capacitor Voltage (V_p) 100 W	1500 W	Efficiency (%)
5	315	n/a	0.08	100	390	98
500	n/a	32	0.79	310	1210	98
25 + j100	n/a	85	0.72	290	1120	98
25 − j100	140	n/a	0.58	100	390	97
250 + j250	n/a	43	0.79	310	1210	98
250 − j250	n/a	22	0.79	310	1210	98

Table 15-6

Component Requirements for Low-Pass Pi-Network Antenna Tuners at 10:1 SWR

Frequency/Z (Ω) 1.8 MHz	Capacitor Input (pF)	Output (pF)	Inductor (μH)	Capacitor Voltage (V_p) 100 W	1500 W	Efficiency (%)
5	5256	500	1.4	100	390	98
500	2602	1000	9.6	310	1200	96
25 + j100	966	1500	12.5	280	1110	97
25 − j100	3410	500	7.5	280	1100	96
250 + j250	1931	1000	11.3	310	1210	97
250 − j250	1284	500	12.9	310	1210	97

Frequency/Z (Ω) 3.5 MHz	Capacitor Input (pF)	Output (pF)	Inductor (μH)	Capacitor Voltage (V_p) 100 W	1500 W	Efficiency (%)
5	2706	500	0.7	100	390	98
500	1287	500	5.1	310	1200	96
25 + j100	643	800	6.2	280	1110	97
25 − j100	1886	300	3.7	280	1430	95
250 + j250	934	500	6.0	310	1200	97
250 − j250	859	300	6.2	310	1200	97

Frequency/Z (Ω) 30 MHz	Capacitor Input (pF)	Output (pF)	Inductor (μH)	Capacitor Voltage (V_p) 100 W	1500 W	Efficiency (%)
5	321	200	0.08	100	390	98
500	118	50	0.7	310	1200	97
25 + j100	103	100	0.7	290	1100	97
25 − j100	205	30	0.5	285	1100	96
250 + j250	71	50	0.8	310	1200	97
250 − j250	77	30	0.8	310	1200	97

Figure 15-8 — Front view of an early homemade antenna tuner. The unit is completely built of surplus parts. Note the handy tuning chart that was part of the BC-375 transmitter tuning drawer.

Figure 15-9 — Inside view of the home brew T-network tuner. The SWR meter (in 2 × 2 × 5 inch box in left partition) and associated circuitry would likely not be needed to use with current transceivers.

Figure 15-10 — Homebrew breadboard T-network tuner made by Barry Shackleford, W6YE. This tuner uses smaller variable capacitors with a voltage rating appropriate for 100 W use. The inductor was homemade, as described in the text. Note the inductance can be changed by moving (with transmitter off) the alligator clip to a different turn.

Figure 15-11 — Another view of Shackleford's T-network tuner.

tuner shown in **Figure 15-12**. This uses two capacitors in parallel, one an old broadcast three-gang unit, making up the single capacitor for the L-network. The smaller capacitor makes it easy to make fine adjustments, once you're close with the larger unit.

Making Tuners for Balanced Loads

Many tuners; home made as well as commercial units, provide for balanced loads by including a balun between an unbalanced tuner and the balanced load. This is an appropriate approach if the load is within perhaps 4:1 of the typical 200 to 50 Ω balun often used for the purpose. If beyond that range, the balun does not perform very well and losses and even damage may result.

A different approach was presented by Richard Measures, AG6K, in a *QST* article some years back.[6] Measures presented a design that first transformed the balanced antenna system load to 50 Ω balanced and then made the transition from balanced to unbalanced using a 1:1 choke balun operating at its design impedance.

Measures used a balanced L-network to perform the transition to 50 Ω and followed it with a coax choke. The schematic is shown in **Figure 15-13**, with a photo of his breadboard version, less balun, in **Figure 15-14**. He went on to show an elegant design suitable for remote control using stepper motors with remote position indicators, available on the ARRL members Web site. However, for many, a duplication of his breadboard design may be more feasible.

Measures found that inductors in the range of 15 to 20 μH maximum inductance were suitable, with a 5 A current rating for 1.5 kW use. Inductors may be found at hamfests, or are available from MFJ (**www.mfjenter-**

they should be fine at the 100 W level. **Figures 15-10** and **15-11** show a T-network tuner that Barry made. Note the simplicity of construction. The only complication may be the homemade inductors. Barry used acrylic stock, cut and notched with his table saw, using a jig to set the

spacing. You could use any technique that allowed the turns to be spaced so that his alligator clip tuning method can be employed. Barry stretched the wire before winding to work harden it and then secured it in his form with hot glue.

Barry also made the L-network

Figure 15-12 — An L-network tuner made by Barry Shackleford, W6YE. The two capacitors are in parallel making a single equivalent capacitance with the smaller one used for fine adjustment.

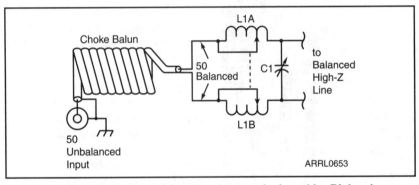

Figure 15-13 — The balanced L-network tuner designed by Richard Measures, AG6K.

Figure 15-14 — Photo of Measures' balanced L-network tuner. The choke-balun is not shown.

prises.com). Suitable sprockets and drive belts to couple the inductors together are available from McMaster-Carr (**www.mcmaster. com**), or they may be coupled end-to-end with some loss of symmetry.

Capacitors should be in the 200 to 300 pF range, with a 1.5 kV rating if used at the 1.5 kW level. Note that both sides of the capacitor are hot with RF, so to avoid burns use an insulated shaft coupling on the way to the knob. Trust me, the set screw in an insulated knob will get you if you don't!

For the choke balun, Measures suggests using solid (not foam) dielectric RG-213, or equivalent, coax wound in a single layer on a 1 foot long, 5 inch diameter, PVC pipe. Other choke configurations may be used, including winding the coax on a ferrite toroid core. An adaptation of the design is to use the L-network to transform to 200 Ω, rather than 50 Ω, and then use a 4:1 balun to finish the impedance transformation and make the transition to unbalanced coax.

As shown, the L-network is designed to transform loads higher then 50 Ω. This is often, but not always the case with ladder and window line systems. If a lower impedance load is encountered, it will be necessary to move the capacitor to the other side of the inductors.

Notes
[1]J. Hallas, W1ZR, "Product Review — A Look at Some High-End Antenna Analyzers" *QST*, May 2005, pp 65-69.
[2]Several versions of *EZNEC* antenna modeling software are available from developer Roy Lewallen, W7EL, at **www.eznec.com**.
[3]R. D. Straw, Editor, *The ARRL Antenna Book,* 21st Edition. Available from your ARRL dealer or the ARRL Bookstore, ARRL order no. 9876. Telephone 860-594-0355, or toll-free in the US 888-277-5289; **www.arrl.org/arrl-store**; **pubsales@arrl.org**.
[4]Note that the value of R will be higher than the dc resistance because of skin effect.
[5]L. McCoy, W1ICP (SK), "The Monimatch," *QST*, Feb 1957, pp 38-40.
[6]Richard Measures, AG6K, "A *Balanced* Balanced Antenna Tuner," *QST*, Feb 1990, pp 28-32.

Hairpin Tuners for Matching Balanced Antenna Systems

Balanced Transmatch designs for 28 to 450 MHz.

John Stanley, K4ERO

Once more, the advantages of ladder line for HF antennas were well presented in July 2008 *QST*.[1] Before WWII surplus brought us cheap coax, balanced feeders were almost always used for VHF as well. In the January 1942 *QST* reproduction that was included with The 2007 ARRL Handbook, we find that both home-brew and commercial VHF gear all used balanced lines.[2] For a given cost, open wire ladder line, window line or even TV twin lead can give you a lower loss installation than trying to buy large diameter coax in an effort to keep the losses to an acceptable level. This is dramatically demonstrated by comparing losses in various line types.[3] So, we wonder, why do so few present-day operators use ladder line or twin lead on the VHF frequencies? Might one reason be the lack of suitable *antenna tuners* (transmatches) for those bands? If balanced tuners were available, would ladder line be as popular at VHF as it has become at HF?

Balanced Tuners for HF Use

The ARRL Handbook, *The ARRL Antenna Book* and other ham publications have always included designs for balanced tuners.[4,5] Adam Nathanson, N4EKV, has one of many good Web sites showing this type of tuner at **www.n4ekv.com/tuners.asp**. I have used tuners like this for years with good results. Figure 1 shows the one I use at up to 100 W on the HF bands.

As noted in Volume 6 of *The ARRL Antenna Compendium*, I lean toward tuners with a fixed link and tapped coil.[6] The match is found by tuning the capacitor and adjusting the output side to

[1]Notes appear on page 36.

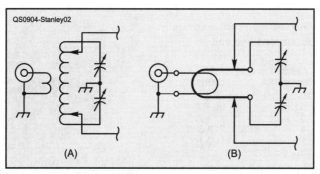

Figure 1 — K4ERO balanced tuner for 60 through 15 meters.

connect to a variable number of turns, keeping the taps equidistant from the coil ends. Other versions use the taps for coarse tune and a variable capacitor in series with the link for finer tuning.

Balanced Tuners for the Higher Frequencies

One of the problems with this type of tuner is that as the frequency goes higher, the number of turns on the coil goes down

rather quickly. By the time you get to 28 MHz, there may be only four turns on the coil. This means that the adjustment *steps* available are very limited. You can tap to either two or four turns, or if you are willing to unbalance the tap positions, or can access the opposite side of the coil, you could use one or three turns. In either case, the operation is compromised. Another approach is to connect one tap to the bottom of the coil, instead of to the top, effectively using fractions of a turn rather than whole turns, but this often is not feasible from a mechanical standpoint. In addition the symmetry and thus the balance are affected. If this type of tuner is to be used on 10 meters and higher, we need to rethink the design.

Figure 2(A) is a schematic of the conventional tapped link coupled tuner. Figure 2(B) is a representation of what I call a *hairpin* tuner. The electrical properties are essentially identical, but the physical layout of the hairpin type is optimum for the higher frequencies. By making the main inductor in the shape of a hairpin, or shorted transmission line, instead of a single layer solenoid coil, as is used in the conventional design, the tuner becomes much easier to build and adjust. The use of a short short-circuited transmission line section as an inductor is nothing new. It has been used for VHF/UHF circuits for many years.

Building Hairpin Tuners

For some time I have been using a hairpin inductor in a balanced tuner for 6 and 10 meters, and recently I built one for each of the 144, 220 and 432 MHz bands. The approach is the same on each frequency. A section of transmission line was used instead of the coil typically used on lower frequencies.

QS0904-Stanley02

(A) (B)

Figure 2 — Balanced tuner configurations. At (A) conventional tapped coil based tuner, at (B) the hairpin equivalent.

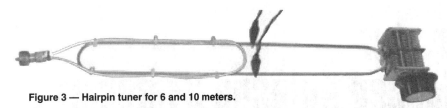

Figure 3 — Hairpin tuner for 6 and 10 meters.

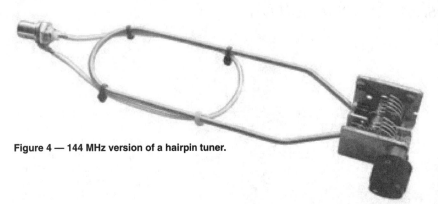

Figure 4 — 144 MHz version of a hairpin tuner.

The capacitor was a split stator or butterfly design. The input link is a single turn inductor that overlaps a portion of the main transmission line inductor and the output taps were taken at whatever point of the hairpin that gives the best match.

The advantage of this layout is that moving the taps to any point on the hairpin is the same as tapping on different numbers of turns on a coil, except that with the hairpin, it is very convenient to make the adjustment in as fine a step as may be desired. In all of my designs, the coupling loop is held to the main hairpin by cable ties. This allows some adjustment of the coupling loop, but holds the loop sufficiently snug so that it is not likely to move around accidentally. Use less loop coupling for higher Q with more selectivity and more loop coupling for lowest loss.

Making them Play

The frequency tuning range percentage will depend on the capacitor used. For widest range, select one with a high minimum to maximum capacitance ratio. All of the capacitors I have tried have provided adequate range to cover the desired amateur band. The range can be extended to cover a second band by putting fixed capacitors in parallel with the variable tuning capacitor. For example, the 6 meter version, shown in Figure 3, works for 10 meters with the addition of a parallel 40 pF fixed ceramic capacitor, while the 220 MHz version, shown in Figure 5, works fine on 2 meters with the addition of a 12 pF ceramic. As it is, the 2 meter version just makes it to 222 MHz, so two bands are possible without switching caps. A single tuner could also work on 10 and 6 meters without switching by careful component selection.

Capacitor Options

The most difficult component to find will likely be the split stator capacitor. There are ways of designing your own capacitor and it is made easier because of the rela-

tively small capacitance required at these frequencies. For all of the designs shown here, I took capacitors from my well stocked junk box. You less well equipped folks will have to search at a hamfest or check out the basement of one of the local old timers. Commercial capacitors are available, but the price may shock you. You could also choose to use a single section capacitor instead of the split stator. In that case, the capacitor shaft and frame will be "hot" and must be floated above ground. You will have to tune it via a long insulated shaft. And, of course, the balance will be somewhat compromised. The method does work and a suitable single section capacitor may be easier to find, however . Alternatively you could use a pair of identical capacitors to ground if you adjusted them each to the same setting or worked out a common shaft arrangement. Fussy, but it could work. Target dimensions and component values for the bands in this range are shown in Table 1.

Inductor Choices

The length of the hairpin will depend on the value of your capacitor. The values below represent tuners I have built and should give you a good starting point. Match the hairpin width to the spacing of the capacitor terminals, or bend the ends of the hairpin in or out at the capacitor end in order to make the connections. Spacing does affect the inductance value so keep it close to what you see in the photos.

My inductors are ⅛ inch diameter brass rod, but they could be soft copper tubing or wire in sizes from 12 gauge up to ¼ inch. Brass welding rods from the hardware store could also be used. A smaller diameter means the hairpin should be shortened a bit as the inductance per inch will be higher. The links should be insulated wire, either enameled or PVC coated or, best of all, Teflon insulated. The 6 meter tuner in Figure 3 uses the shield of Teflon coax as the link. My links do not make electrical contact anywhere with the main hairpin. The coax shield and center of the hairpin could both

---

Table 1 ———————————————————————

Hairpin Tuner Component Values, Dimensions and Frequency Range

Band	Capacitor Value (pF/Section)*	Inductor Length (Inches)**	Tuning Range (MHz)***
10 Meters	95-170	15	26-34
6 Meters	15-90	15	36-90
2 Meters	3-20	6	110-225
222 MHz	3-10	4	220-330
432 MHz	3-4	1.5	390-440

*Effective capacity is ½ of the value/section.
**All inductors made of ⅛ inch brass rod.
***Range may by reduced or shifted by reactive loads.

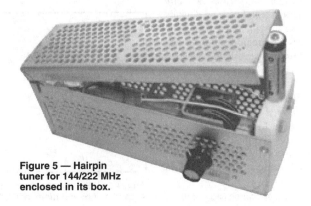

Figure 5 — Hairpin tuner for 144/222 MHz enclosed in its box.

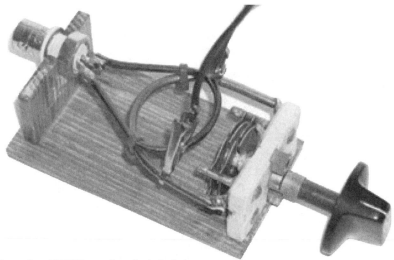

Figure 6 — 432 MHz version of a hairpin tuner.

be grounded to a chassis, if desired.

Tuning Up

Tuning consists of setting the taps to an intermediate position and adjusting the capacitor for minimum SWR. If SWR is not as low as desired, move the taps a bit either towards or away from the capacitor and readjust the capacitor. You should be able to find tap settings that allow the SWR to be reduced to 1:1.

Safety Considerations

Note that neither of the tuners described above are shown installed within a chassis of any kind. This is to show the construction more clearly. Also, I must admit that during tests, I got away with this because I used low power and am very careful not to touch the *hot* parts of the circuit. I also have a non-metallic operating desk. The open construction is useful during experiments.

I definitely do not recommend this approach for general use. You will want to put your tuner in a shielded box of some kind, probably with a hinged lid to allow you to move the taps as shown in Figure 5.

You should *never* adjust the tap clips with power applied. The tuning shaft should be brought out through the enclosure where an insulated knob should be installed for tuning even though with a split stator capacitor the shaft should be at ground potential. For high power, the use of a suitable enclosure is essential, especially if the tuner is to be installed close to the operating position. This is to prevent RF burns from contact as well as exposure to excess RF levels.

Remember that your body is more susceptible to pick up from VHF fields than is the case at HF. If you put the tuner well away from the operating position in a place that is protected from access by family members or pets, you may be able to use a somewhat more open construction as is sometimes done with conventional home brew tuners. Radiation from an unenclosed tuner of any type can be enough to cause interference with nearby electronics devices and could cause fires if anything flammable comes in contact with the hot parts of the circuit.

These tuners have been tested with 100 W on 10 and 6 meters, 50 W on 2 meters and 20 W on 70 cm, the maximum output of

my rig. For higher power, the designs can be scaled, remembering that the bigger it gets, the lower the frequency for the same geometry. Thus, a design similar to that used here for 432 MHz, but three times larger, would probably work fine with a full kW, but on 144 MHz. Since my 20 W, 432 MHz design uses an inductor that is about as short as is practical (see Figure 6), getting up to 1 kW at 432 MHz, might prove difficult with this design. At the least, a different type of capacitor would be required.

I hope that these simple to build and adjust tuners will start a trend towards greater use of balanced feeders on the higher frequencies just as ladder line has become the favorite for many on the lower bands.

Notes
[1]J. Hallas, W1ZR, "Getting on the Air—Your Second HF Antenna," *QST*, Jul 2008, pp 69-70.
[2]B. Goodman, W1JPE, "Receivers for 112-Mc. Emergency Work," *QST*, Jan 1942, pp 18-25, 74-75.
[3]*The ARRL Handbook for Radio Communications*, 2009 Edition, Figure 21.4. Available from your ARRL dealer or the ARRL Bookstore, ARRL order no. 0261 (Hardcover 0292). Telephone 860-594-0355, or toll-free in the US 888-277-5289; **www.arrl.org/shop**; **pubsales@arrl.org**.
[4]See Note 3, p 21.13.
[5]R. D. Straw, Editor, *The ARRL Antenna Book*, 21st Edition, p 25-3. Available from your ARRL dealer or the ARRL Bookstore, ARRL order no. 9876. Telephone 860-594-0355, or toll-free in the US 888-277-5289; **www.arrl.org/shop**; **pubsales@arrl.org**.
[6]J. Stanley, K4ERO, "The Filtuner," *ARRL Antenna Compendium, Volume 6*. Available from your ARRL dealer or the ARRL Bookstore, ARRL order no. 7431. Telephone 860-594-0355, or toll-free in the US 888-277-5289; **www.arrl.org/shop**; **pubsales@arrl.org**.

John Stanley, K4ERO, holds an Amateur Extra class license and has been licensed for over 50 years. He has worked as a broadcast engineer most of his life, mainly with religious shortwave stations in many parts of the world. He graduated from MIT in 1962 with a BSEE degree. John is an ARRL Technical Adviser. He and his wife, Ruth, WB4LUA, live in Rising Fawn, Georgia. You can reach John at 524 White Pine Ln, Rising Fawn, GA 30738 or at **jnrstanley@alum.MIT.edu**.

Review Questions

15-1 What are some major challenges involved with building an antenna tuner?

15-2 Under what conditions is a special purpose tuner a viable option?

15-3 Why might you decide not to include 160 meters in your tuner design?

APPENDIX A

Making Sense of Decibels

Joel R. Hallas, W1ZR

Much of the technical data found in *QST* and other ARRL publications is expressed in decibels, generally shown as *dB*. Contrary to the belief of some, this is not done to mystify beginners, but rather is intended to make comparisons easier and avoid the use of very large or small numbers.

So What's this Decibels Business All About?

Decibels are just a way of expressing ratios, often power ratios. If we are looking at the gain of an amplifier stage, the pattern of an antenna or the loss of a transmission line we are generally interested in the ratio of the power out to the power in, or the ratio of the power in front of a beam antenna to that coming from the back. These are some of the places that we will find the results expressed in dB.

Decibels are a logarithmic function. Logarithms are a handy mathematical tool based on exponents. An important feature of logarithms is that multiplication can be performed by adding the logarithmic quantities instead of multiplying them. Similarly, divisions can be accomplished by subtracting in the same manner. This becomes a benefit if you are dealing with multiple stages of amplification and attenuation — as we often are in radios — snatching a minuscule signal from the ether — amplifying and processing it so we can hear it out the loudspeaker. Instead of having to multiply and divide at each stage to keep track of the progress of our signal processing — often with signal levels with many zeros to the right of the decimal point — we can just tally all the dB and have total gain of the system.

So How do We Compute the Decibels?

The *deci* in decibels refers to a factor of ¹⁄₁₀, as in *deciliters* for ¹⁄₁₀ of a liter, while the *bel* relates to the idea of a logarithmic ratio, originally used to define sound power.

- To convert a power ratio into decibels, just:
  1. Find the base 10 logarithm of the power ratio.
  2. Multiply by 10.

For example, if we have an amplifier with a power gain of 275, we find the logarithm of 275 (see below, if you don't do logs in your head) to be 2.44. We multiply by 10 and the result is that a power gain of 275 can be represented as 24.4 dB.

- To convert decibels to a power ratio, we do the opposite:

Figure 1 — The *Windows Scientific Calculator* ready to calculate the effect of a 2 dB cable loss.

  1. Divide by 10.
  2. Find the base 10 antilog of the result.

Note that the base 10 antilog of a number is just 10 raised to the power of the number. This is also something you probably don't do in your head, so let's see how to easily perform the computations.

Understanding a few characteristics of logs will help avoid problems interpreting results. Note that a gain of 0 dB means that there is no change to the signal — not that the signal has vanished! The other important fact is that a power ratio of less than one (a loss rather than a gain) is represented as a negative number in decibels.

Enter the *Windows Scientific Calculator*

In the *very* old days, engineers and technicians used tables to make accurate logarithmic calculations, and mechanical slide rules if three significant digits was sufficient precision.[1] Starting around 1970, scientific calculators became available. Initially they were expensive typewriter-sized devices that were typically shared within an engineering department. Within a few years pocket-sized units were available for less than $200, and now everyone could make calculations to a precision of nine significant digits, whether warranted by the data accuracy or not. Tables and slide rules were relegated to the pages of history with spark transmitters.

The dawn of the reasonably priced personal computer seemed to push the fancy scientific calculator out of sight only about 10 years later. Unfortunately, for many functions a calculator may be a better choice, and decibel calcula-

[1]See, for example, *Standard Mathematical Tables*, CRC Press, any edition. In addition to tables of logarithms and trigonometric functions, it includes many handy formulas from geometry, trigonometry and calculus.

tions may be one. The calculations may be easily performed on a PC by putting the equations in cells of an Excel spreadsheet, but not everyone can do that without a lot of thought.

If you have a suitable scientific calculator, that should easily make the calculations. Not all have an ANTILOG button, but if not, they will likely have a button that says X^Y, which can be used as above. If you don't have a handheld calculator, you may not know that there is a very capable one included as an "accessory" within the Microsoft *Windows* operating system! Just click START then ALL PROGRAMS then ACCESSORIES. You should find an icon for the *Windows Calculator*. You could open it, but why not drag it onto your desktop first.

On first opening, you may find a fourfunction grocery store type calculator. Have no fear, just click on VIEW then SCIENTIFIC to get the one you want. It should look about like Figure 1.

Give it a Test Drive

Let's say you have a mismatched coax cable with a loss of 2 dB. You may want to know how many of the 100 W from your transmitter actually reach your antenna. Remember a 2 dB loss is a "gain" of –2 dB! We'll go through the inverse dB calculation of column 2. Using your *Windows Calculator*, either hit 2 on your keyboard, or:

- Click on the 2 on the calculator "keypad," then:
- Click on the +/– key; the display should show – 2, as in Figure 1.
- Click on the / key to select the "divide by" operation. Enter the digits 1 and 0 for the number 10 and hit ENTER or =. Make note of the result (–0.2) or store it in memory (M+).
- Enter the digits 1 and 0 for the number 10.
- Click on X^Y to raise 10 to a power.
- Enter your earlier result, –.2 and hit ENTER.
- The display should show 0.63095734448 019324943436013662234 or about 0.63. That is the fraction of your power left after a 2 dB loss. That means your antenna sees 63 W and 37 W is heating your transmission line.

While you are using the *Windows Scientific Calculator* look over its other features. It provides painless conversion between decimal and binary, octal or hex numbers, for example.

Joel R. Hallas, W1ZR, is QST Technical Editor. He can be reached at **w1zr@arrl.org**. **QST**

Index

Notes

FEEDBACK

Please use this form to give us your comments on this book and what you'd like to see in future editions, or e-mail us at **pubsfdbk@arrl.org** (publications feedback). If you use e-mail, please include your name, call, e-mail address and the book title, edition and printing in the body of your message. Also indicate whether or not you are an ARRL member.

Where did you purchase this book? ☐ From ARRL directly ☐ From an ARRL dealer

Is there a dealer who carries ARRL publications within:

☐ 5 miles ☐ 15 miles ☐ 30 miles of your location? ☐ Not sure.

License class:

☐ Novice ☐ Technician ☐ Technician with code ☐ General ☐ Advanced ☐ Amateur Extra

Name _____ ARRL member? ☐ Yes ☐ No

_____ Call Sign _____

Address _____

City, State/Province, ZIP/Postal Code _____

Daytime Phone (   ) _____ Age _____

If licensed, how long? _____

Other hobbies _____ E-mail _____

_____

Occupation _____

From _____

_____

_____

EDITOR, THE ARRL GUIDE TO ANTENNA TUNERS
ARRL—THE NATIONAL ASSOCIATION FOR AMATEUR RADIO
225 MAIN STREET
NEWINGTON CT 06111-1494

please fold and tape